Great Pioneer Heroes

V 14

Great Pioneer
Heroes —Edited by Rafer Brent

TRUE STORIES OF THE MEN WHO MADE AMERICA

BARTHOLOMEW HOUSE • NEW YORK

Library of Congress Catalog Card Number: 58-7883
Manufactured in the United States of America

Contents

c.1

Illustration Credits

Frontiersman—The Story of Daniel Boone
from a painting by John Flaherty, Jr.

Simon Kenton's War with the Indians
from a painting by Slayton Underhill

Davy Crockett—King of the Wild Frontier
from a painting by Jack Hearne

The Saga of Sam Houston
from a painting by Herb Mott

The Saga of Jim Bridger
from a painting by Brendan Lynch

John C. Frémont—Pathfinder
from a painting by Brendan Lynch

The Kit Carson Nobody Knows
from a painting by Jack Hearne

Cover
from a painting by Stan Borack

Great Pioneer Heroes

Frontiersman
The Story of Daniel Boone

By JACK PEARL

Sharpshooter, Indian fighter, and the first of the great American trail blazers, he turned his back on profit, power, and glory to get a little elbow room.

Peddler John Finley gave a hearty belch and pushed the jug back across the rough board table to the big man seated opposite him. "You ain't changed much in fourteen years, Dan'l." He studied his friend's long horse face with fond recollection. It was a little leaner, perhaps; the tanned, pock-marked flesh drawn tighter over the high cheekbones, the hollow cheeks accentuating the long, jutting jaw. It was a face with character. The nose was strong, the eyes blue and deep-set. "I never figured to find you settled down in the Yadkin Valley with a wife and family, Dan'l, you with the itchy feet." As Daniel's wife, Rebecca, turned away briefly from the wood stove, he coughed and added loudly, "But the moment I gazed on this lass of yours, I saw the reason."

"You're wastin' your breath, Mr. Finley," Rebecca said dryly. "I don't aim to buy none of your pots."

Daniel Boone laughed and combed back his shaggy red hair with his fingers. "She is quite a lass, ain't she, John?" He shoved the jug back to the little chubby, red-faced peddler. "Have another drink. Yup, I'm pleased with things the way they are. I got me a good horse, a good wife, and a good gun. That's all a man needs to be happy." He cast a loving glance at the long rifle hanging on pegs above the fireplace. "Me and old Tick-Licker, we get to go huntin' most every day." He walked past Finley to the open door and stood gazing across the rolling country to the northwest at the mountains shrouded in blue haze that ran across the horizon like a mammoth wall. He was so absorbed that he didn't hear John Finley come up behind him to stand at his shoulder.

"You don't fool me," the peddler said in a low voice. "It's been fourteen years, but the fire's still there. I can see it. You're burnin' to know what's on the other side of them mountains. *Ken-ta-ke,* the Injuns call it."

"Caintuck." Daniel mouthed the South Carolina corruption of the Indian word. "You know, John, I been to Florida and Tennessee, but lots of men had been there before me. Ain't no elbow room. Over thar it's different. No white men ever set foot on the other side of them mountains. I keep thinkin', wouldn't it be something to stand in a place where no one else has ever stood before you? Like you was all alone in the world, the only one who mattered. A man could breathe there." He turned back past Finley to the table, picked up the jug, and took a long swig. "Well," he sighed, "it ain't no good thinkin' about it. Less you can sprout wings and fly over them peaks, there's only one way into that land—down the Ohio River where the Cherokees will kill you on sight."

"I been down the Ohio as far as any man, I guess," Finley said. "Tradin' with the Cherokees. I've heard tell some stories about *Ken-ta-ke*. They say the grass is blue and—"

"Do tell," Rebecca sniffed as she set the table for supper.

Finley cast a reproachful look at her—"and there's springs where the salt bubbles out of the ground and all you have to do is sack it up and carry it away."

"Jiminy!" Young Israel's black eyes were as big and round as frying pans.

Daniel's face was as eager as the boy's. "Becky, did you hear that? Why, it must be like one of them storybook countries."

Rebecca emptied a pot of steaming potatoes into a wooden bowl. "That's right, Dan'l, a fairy tale book."

Daniel walked back to the doorway again, pounding his fist into his other hand, and stared out at the distant hills. "Oh lordie, what I wouldn't give to see that."

Finley helped himself to the jug once more. "I've heerd tell other things, too," he said slyly. "You know what the Warrior's Trail is?"

"Can't say as I do," Daniel answered abstractedly.

"They say the Injuns know of a secret pass through them mountains."

"Just wild talk," Rebecca said suspiciously.

Daniel swung around interestedly. "You figure it's so, John?"

Finley shrugged. "There's one thing about Injuns, they ain't givin' to lyin'! Someday, when I get me a stake and some partners, I aim to find out. If a trappin' party could get into that country, they could pack out enough skins in one winter to make 'em rich."

The sparks were snapping in Daniel's eyes now. "It wouldn't be in the Blue Ridge or the Clinch Range. I know them mountains like the back of my hand. But the Cumberlands, now, there's where to look for it, in the Cumberlands. By God, John, if there is such a pass, we'll find it."

Mrs. Boone looked wearily at her daughter Jemima. "I would have done better to buy one of his old kettles 'fore he could get his foot in the door and see your daddy."

On May 1, 1769, a party of trappers; consisting of Daniel Boone, Daniel's brother-in-law, John Stuart, John Finley, and three men named Mooney, Holden, and Cooley; headed west out of the Yadkin Valley to search for the secret route into *Ken-ta-ke*. In the doorway of her cabin, Rebecca Boone watched them ride across a hump in the road, out of sight. The last thing she saw was the high crown of Daniel's store-bought black beaver hat perched straight on his head in the sedate manner of an opera hat. With his long braided hair, buckskins, and moccasins, it lent a comical touch to his appearance, but he stubbornly refused to adopt the conventional coonskin cap of the period. Rebecca smiled sadly to herself as she watched him go and shook her head. "I never did see a man who needed so much elbow room."

Where the southwest tip of Virginia forks the boundaries of Tennessee and Kentucky, there is a narrow breach thirteen hundred feet up in the mountain wall known as the Cumberland Gap. This natural pathway between Kentucky and Virginia had been discovered in 1750 by a surveying party, but Daniel Boone didn't know that, and the wonder and thrill of discovery were his as, on a sunny spring morning in May, he and the other trappers milled around the mouth of the pass, laughing, shouting, and congratulating themselves.

Daniel squinted up the slope through the strong sunlight. "That looks like a well-used path."

John Finley nodded soberly, "The Warrior's Trail. And it looks too well used for my taste. If the Injuns catch us in their hunting grounds . . ." he let it trail off ominously.

"The hell with the Injuns!" John Stuart swung into his saddle and dug his heels into the horse. "Let's see what this Caintuck looks like."

Much later they stood on the high ground at the other end of the gap, gazing across the rolling hills and plains that stretched away beyond the treetops. Everything seemed to be wrapped in purple haze. "You know, John," Daniel said reverently to Finley, "I wish Becky could see this. She'd be sorry she was so snappish to you, I reckon. The grass *is* blue."

The trappers established their camp on a small creek in the forest close to the Warrior's Trail. At intervals of a few miles on either side of it, they set up small base camps and strung out their traplines. Game was abundant, and each week that passed swelled the bales of hides stored in the main camp. The summer went by uneventfully, without any sign of Indians. The only note of excitement was provided by a bear who sneaked into camp early one morning and carried off Daniel's cherished high hat while he was bathing in the creek. With a whoop and a roar, Daniel leaped to the bank, grabbed old Tick-Licker, and chased after the thief—stark naked. Mooney and Cooley, just returning from a morning hunt, were so badly shaken by the naked specter flashing by them that they finished off a pint of medicinal spirits before breakfast. Stuart and Finley picked up their rifles and set out after Daniel and the bear. The sound of a single shot spurred them on faster. About a half-mile from camp, they burst into a clearing and were treated to a rare sight. A dead bear lay sprawled on the ground, and standing over it was Daniel Boone, his nakedness now somewhat dignified by a rather forlorn and dirty chapeau.

Daniel grinned when he caught sight of his friends. "That damned bear sure know'd class when he seed it." He smoothed out the prized headpiece tenderly with his fingers. "Will one of you fellers lend me your long knife?"

John Finley unsheathed a treacherous-looking foot of steel with a bone handle. Daniel took it and, turning to a nearby tree, began to carve block letters in the bark.

"What in tarnation!" Stuart exchanged a blank look with Finley; then they both stared at Daniel with their mouths open. After a few minutes, he stepped back from the tree, unveiling a crude inscription he had gouged into the trunk: "D Boon cilled a bar on this Tree."

John Finley whistled through his teeth. "Lord, it's a lucky thing you're handier with a gun than you are with letters, Dan'l."

Daniel laughed. "My paw used to say, 'Let the gals do the spellin' and Dan'l do the shootin'.'"

On the last day of October, the trappers were awakened

by big wet snowflakes plopping down on their faces. "Bout time we pulled out of here," Stuart grunted as they ate breakfast. "Before winter sets in." The other men nodded. Finley glanced at their bales of hides stacked under a lean-to. "We got more skins than we can carry as it is."

Daniel frowned. "I was hopin' to get me one really fine buffalo hide to take back to Becky."

"Ain't you shot enough of them poor critters?" Stuart asked with a laugh.

"Well, I want a really big bull," Daniel said. "Last night when I was checking my traps in that little valley to the north, I spied a big herd grazin' there. If it hadn't been so close to dark I would'a had me one." That afternoon he persuaded Stuart to return with him to the spot, a cleavage between two ranges of grassy, rolling hills. In the past, it had always been their custom to hunt from horseback. This time Daniel suggested they tether their mounts at the mouth of the valley and approach the herd on foot. "In this high grass we ought to be able to get right on top of 'em 'fore they know it," he explained to Stuart. "When you're on a horse they can see you comin' a half-mile off and then it's all over. The only ones these pack horses of ours can run down is the runts and sickly females. This time I aim to get me a brute."

Keeping low in the grass, they moved silently toward the buffalo grazing about a quarter of a mile downwind from them. When they were about one hundred yards from the herd, Daniel stopped. "This is plenty close enough, John," he whispered. "Don't want to take a chance of stampedin' 'em!" Carefully, he measured out a charge from his powder horn into the breech of the rifle. Suddenly Stuart gripped his arm. "Dan'l, look! They must've got on to us." Several of the big shaggy beasts had their heads in the air, sensitive nostrils sifting the scents.

Daniel squinted through the grass. "That cain't be," he said. But as the buffalo began to bellow and stomp the dust, his eyes narrowed in concern. "Unless . . . maybe there's Injuns up ahead there."

"We better get out of here," John Stuart made a move to

turn back. At that moment, a large bull that Daniel had picked out as his target let out a tremendous roar and began to pound the earth with his front hoofs. As though this were a signal, the herd swung clumsily in his direction. Then, as Daniel and Stuart watched in horror, the buffaloes stampeded toward them. Panicked, Stuart threw down his rifle and started to run. Daniel reached out and grabbed his shirt. "You damn fool! You can't outrun 'em. We only got one chance." He dropped to one knee and raised Tick-Licker to his shoulder. Stuart watched numbly, certain that his brother-in-law had gone mad to think he could stop that charging mass of beef and muscle. The big bull who led the herd was bearing down directly on them, about ten yards out in front of the others. When he was about twenty feet away, Daniel pulled the trigger; the explosion burst unheard beneath the thunder of the churning hooves. The big bull ducked his head low and stumbled, legs folding beneath him. He pitched forward and tumbled end over end until he came to rest in a quivering heap about five feet in front of the two trappers.

"C'mon, John, get in close!" Daniel scrambled forward and crouched against the still quivering mountain of flesh. Stuart dove after him, head first, as the storm broke around them. Alarmed by the collapse of their leader, the buffaloes in the front ranks shied away to the left and right, avoiding his carcass. Almost before the two hunters realized it, the herd was past, the grass behind the animals leveled as flat as if a threshing machine had mowed the field. Shakily, Stuart and Daniel got to their feet. With his hands on his hips, Daniel stared solemnly at the hills to the west. Stuart laughed nervously. "Hey, Dan'l, they went that-away." He jerked his thumb at the clouds of dust rising in back of the disappearing herd.

"It ain't them I'm worried about," Daniel said slowly. "It's what riled 'em up that bothers me. C'mon, we'd better be getting back."

It was almost dark when the two men rode into the main camp. The camp was deserted, but it didn't concern them unduly since the trappers usually made a final check of their traplines before dark. What did puzzle Daniel was the silence.

Even the crickets were strangely mute. Then a hoot owl screamed in the woods nearby. Another one answered him from the opposite side of the clearing. The hair on Daniel's neck bristled. In a low voice he said to Stuart, "We got company. Mosey down to the stream like we was gonna wash. And take your time." Stuart nodded slightly, and they walked on at a leisurely pace. But before they had taken many steps, shapes emerged from the shadows around them. "Stop, white men!" a guttural voice called out sharply, and they found themselves menaced by a ring of muskets.

"Better do as they say, John," Daniel cautioned. He held up his hands, palms out, in the Indian peace sign. The leader advanced toward him. He was a big man, lean and heavily muscled. Daniel recognized him as a Shawnee by his scalp lock topped with a feather. "Me Captain Will," he said in fairly good English.

Daniel made a show of indignation. "We come to your country as friends. Is it honorable to greet us with guns?"

Captain Will smiled, "Me not so stupid. You not, either. No man who reaches in hive for honey expect bees to treat him kindly. You our prisoners."

It was with sick hearts that Daniel and Stuart watched their bales of hides strapped on the backs of the Indians' horses. "A half-year's work," Stuart groaned. "And all our horses too."

Daniel shrugged. "I wonder what happened to Finley and the others."

Stuart's face darkened. "Yellow skunks, that's what they are, running out on us like that."

"I dunno. We ain't got no cause to be proud, walkin' into that trap like we done!" At that moment Captain Will came up and motioned for them to mount. "We go now," he said.

For six days and nights, the trappers were ideal prisoners, even professing that they were glad to be captured. "I can't wait to see my old friend Simon Girty again," Daniel told Stuart, loud enough so that Captain Will could hear him. In the eyes of the Indians, no man could boast of a greater honor than to be a friend of the famed renegade white man.

Gradually, the Indians relaxed their vigilance. It was their custom at night to tie each prisoner by leather thongs to two braves who slept on either side of him. But on the seventh night, Captain Will waived this formality. Daniel and Stuart were permitted to sleep side by side with the Shawnees arranged in a circle around them. When the last ember in the fire winked out and Daniel was sure that the Indians all were asleep, he rolled over close to Stuart and pinched his arm. Stuart acknowledged the signal with a nudge of his elbow. There was no need for further communication. Both men's minds were tuned to one thought—escape. And both realized that this ideal combination of circumstances might never present itself again. The fire was out and the moon was dark.

Daniel sat up slowly and threw off his blanket. Next to him he could make out Stuart fumbling with his moccasins. He nodded with satisfaction. His brother-in-law was a seasoned woodsman who knew what had to be done without being told.

The edge of the forest was about thirty feet away, and between it and them were the Shawnees, their senses sharpened to a fine animal sensitivity, sleeping lightly with one ear always alert for danger. The snap of a twig, the crunch of dirt, the friction of rough buckskin trousers, the slightest accent on the quiet of the night would betray their plan.

It was about a dozen steps to the forest and safety, and between each step Daniel lived a lifetime. A shape materialized out of the darkness in front of him; a sleeping Shawnee was sprawled in his path. He made a rapid calculation. One long step if he stepped over him, three extra steps if he went around him. Reluctant to waste a single step, he stretched one leg across the man. At that moment the Shawnee stirred abruptly in his sleep and rolled over, flinging one arm out of the blanket. His fingers brushed the fringe on Daniel's buckskin pants. Daniel crouched low over him, his hands poised inches away from the defenseless throat. Minutes went by, and the deep rhythmic breathing did not change. Daniel's muscles relaxed. Quickly he stepped over the sleeping Shawnee and padded silently to the edge of the wood. A minute later he was joined by John Stuart. Together the two men moved off into the trees.

"I thought we were goners for a minute there," Stuart whispered weakly. "Lucky for us that Injun was a sound sleeper."

Daniel grinned in the darkness. "Lucky for him, too."

Two days later they arrived at their old campsite. Finley and the other three had gathered in their traps and were preparing to head back to the Yadkin Valley. When Stuart accused them of cowardice for not making any attempt to rescue Daniel and him from the Indians or to save their furs, Finley shrugged. "All we could have hoped to accomplish by startin' trouble was a quick scalpin' for you boys. They had us outnumbered bad. Besides, we figured two men would have a better chance of escapin' than six."

"Cain't argue with that," Daniel laughed. "Here we are to prove it."

Mooney looked worried. "We'd better get out of here fast. Won't be long before those Injuns come after you two."

Daniel shook his head. "I don't reckon so. They'll figger we won't stop runnin' till we reach Virginia. Besides, they're loaded down with furs."

"*Our* furs," Cooley echoed gloomily. "Every time I think of all that money, I could cut my throat with my own knife."

Daniel's eyes were bright. "Thar's plenty more where they come from. Why, by the end of the winter we ought to be doin' right well again."

"Spend the winter here?" Stuart asked unbelievingly. "You plumb out of your mind, Dan'l?"

"Why not?" Daniel demanded excitedly. "The Injuns won't be botherin' us again until spring. Anyways, I think it would be a lot of fun to spend a winter in this country." He breathed deeply of the spicy air in the pine grove. "A man can really breathe here."

The other trappers looked at one another in bewilderment. "You think we come all the way out here for fun?" Cooley said angrily. "Leave our families and risk losing our scalps for fun?"

" 'Course not," Daniel explained patiently. "A man's gotta make a livin', that's for certain. But that ain't to say he can't enjoy himself while he's doin' it."

That afternoon the decision was taken out of their hands when Squire Boone, Daniel's brother, arrived from South Carolina with fresh horses and supplies. "Now we gotta stay," Daniel gloated like a small boy.

But the winter months were lean for trapping, and when spring came, their stockpile of hides was considerably smaller than the one the Indians had appropriated. Late in March, John Stuart set out to check his traps one morning and never returned. Although they searched the woods for days, they never found any trace of him. Fearful that the Shawnees had come back to stalk them, Finley, Mooney, Holden, and Cooley took their share of the furs and headed for home.

In May, Daniel sent Squire east to sell their furs, pay off their debts, and pack in more supplies. "I don't want to leave you here all alone, Dan'l," his brother protested. "Suppose you get sick? Suppose you get lost in these woods like poor Stuart?"

Daniel grinned. "Ain't never been lost in my life, Squire." He stroked his chin reflectively. "Though I do own to bein' bewildered onct for three days. Now, don't you go frettin' over me."

Nevertheless, Daniel was on Squire's mind a great deal on his journey back to the Yadkin Valley. When he told Rebecca Boone that Daniel had decided to stay behind and mind their traplines, she was furious. "I don't know what ails that man. He won't be satisfied till he's lyin' cold under the ground. Well, I don't care. If the Injuns get 'im, it will serve 'im right. A thirty-six-year-old man with a family and responsibilities runnin' around like a boy playin' in the woods." She sighed. "His maw warned me I was makin' a mistake when I married up with him. He just never grow'd up."

But a few days later, when Squire was making ready to leave on the return trip, Rebecca came to him with lowered eyes. "Tell him we miss him, Squire. Tell him if he don't come back to us real soon, we'll go out to him."

"I'll tell him, Becky." Squire busied himself with a buckle on his saddle, pretending that he didn't see the tears streaking down her cheeks.

Squire made good time back to Kentucky. As he neared the rendezvous spot just off the Warrior's Trail, his heart began to pump faster. For several nights, his sleep had been tormented by violent nightmares: Dan'l, a wild-eyed, gibbering maniac, driven mad by the crush of all this solitude; Dan'l, a wasted shadow of skin and bone, ravaged by fever and delirium; Dan'l, a heap of white bones picked clean by the buzzards.

Ascending the last hill that separated him from the camp, his breath caught in his throat, and he felt as if a piece of ice was sliding down his backbone. Floating to him on the summer breeze came the sound of a human voice. It was a weird, frightening sound, part moan, part screech, rising and falling with passion and rhythm. He dropped the horse's bridle and sprinted up to the summit of the hill. The sight he beheld was like nothing he had been imagining.

There, on the bank of the little stream below him, was his brother Daniel, ruddier and healthier than Squire had ever remembered him, bellowing at the top of his lungs while he waltzed around with old Tick-Licker held at arm's length like some beautiful woman at the Governor's Ball.

When he had recovered from the shock, Squire cupped his hands to his mouth and screamed, "God damn it, Dan'l! You sound like a bull moose in matin' season. I like to have died from fright."

Without breaking step, Daniel looked up the slope and grinned. "You never did have much of an ear for good music, Squire."

That summer the trapping was good, and when fall came, the Boone brothers had more hides than their horses could pack out. But a few days before they started east, disaster struck again. Daniel and Squire returned to the camp late one night to find it overrun with Shawnees. They got away without being captured, but Squire was bitter. As they rode west through the Gap, he spat contemptuously. "Caintuck! Let the Injuns keep it."

Daniel stepped on a rise and looked back at the thick green forests, the rich rolling plains, and the blue mountains in the distance. "Damn it, Squire," he said wistfully. "I'm gonna miss it, so help me."

Squire stared at him strangely. "You all right in the head, Dan'l? Two years, almost, you spent here, and what have you got to show for it?"

Daniel tapped his chest, over his heart. "What I got in here, you can't buy for any money, Squire."

Times were hard for the settlers in the Yadkin Valley, as they were for most of the colonists on the eastern seaboard in 1770. Game was becoming scarce, and what meager profits they could squeeze out of their farms were devoured by soaring taxes. With an eye for the discontent around him, Daniel talked incessantly about the promised land that was ripe for the taking in *Ken-ta-ke*. It seemed to Rebecca that whenever she looked out the door, there would be Daniel surrounded by a dozen eager listeners under the big elm in their front yard. "You make me sick," she told him irritably one night. "Caintuck! Caintuck! Don't you know nothin' else to talk about?"

He came up in back of her at the stove and put his hands lightly on her shoulders. "Becky," he said in a low voice, "some of the boys are thinkin' about goin' into that country. Settlin' down there and farmin' the land." He hesitated. "They're lookin' for somebody to guide 'em."

" 'Course you had nothin' to do with the idea," she said bitterly.

"Well, I just happened to overhear the talk and—"

She whirled around to face him, her eyes filling with angry tears. "Oh, stop it, Dan'l! You know full well you're the one that cooked up the whole scheme. You ain't had a moment's peace since you came back from that horrible place. Cain't wait to get away from your responsibilities again, can you?"

"Now, Becky," Daniel said with the injured pride of a

small boy. "I never had any such idea. The fact of the matter is I'm gettin' too old to be runnin' around the woods. My back's been botherin' me lately too." He put a hand gingerly to his spine.

Rebecca shook her finger in his face. "Fiddlesticks! Now, you listen to me, Dan'l Boone. If you're fixin' to run off from us again, you got another think comin'."

"There you go, imagining things again."

"Next time you go gallivantin', I'm goin' with you. See how you like that!"

"Why, that would please me fine." He wrinkled up his nose thoughtfully. "But like I said, I never gave the matter any thought at all. I suppose if they was to ask me—" A knock at the door interrupted him.

"Now who could that be?" Becky hurried across the room and opened the door. A tall thin man with blond hair touched his cap, "Dan'l in, Miz Boone?"

"Yes, come in, Mr. Johnson."

Daniel walked up and peered over her shoulder. "How are you, Jack? Come in for a drink?"

"Thanks no, Dan'l," the man replied. "I'm in a hurry. But I just wanted to let you know it was all right about those horses."

"What horses?" Rebecca asked before Daniel could answer him.

Mr. Johnson smiled, "The ones I'm gonna lend him for you and the children when we leave for Caintuck on Friday." He winked at Daniel and flapped his arms like a rooster. "Plenty of elbow room, eh, Dan'l?"

"Ooof!" Daniel grunted as Rebecca's elbow dug sharply into the pit of his stomach.

Late in September, 1773, the Boones and fifteen other families left the Yadkin Valley for *Ken-ta-ke*. The expedition miscarried while they were still in Virginia. One night after they had camped on the banks of the Clinch River, Daniel's son, James, and two other young men rode off to a nearby settlement for some supplies. On the way back, they were ambushed by marauding Indians and killed. The other settlers were thrown into a panic over the incident. It was a grim introduction to the dangers that faced them across the Cumberlands, and many of them turned back to the Yadkin.

Daniel was filled with remorse and grief over the death of his older son. "You must hate me, Becky," he said somberly to his wife. "It's like I handed the boy over to them savages with my own hands."

"Dan'l, don't," Rebecca said gently.

"It's true, though. I brought you here, didn't I? Isn't that why he's dead?"

"That's foolish, Dan'l. He was here because he wanted to be with you. Like we all want to be with you." Her eyes were tender.

Daniel pounded his fist on his knee in an agony of frustration. "But why am I here? Why?" He shook his head. "I'm like some kind of an animal. I could never stand to be closed in by people and houses. I gotta be free."

Rebecca blinked back the tears. "You can't help bein' like you are, Dan'l. A man has to be himself."

His jaw tightened. "But a man can change. We'll go back to the Yadkin. Maybe we'll go north. I'll get me a city job, just you wait and see."

In spite of the ache in her heart, Rebecca had to smile. "You'd look mighty swell with that high fancy hat of yours, Dan'l."

"You think I'm joshin' you."

"No, Dan'l, I believe you'd really try, but it wouldn't be any use. The city ain't for you. You're a woodsman. Besides, if we went back now it would be such a waste. We've given our boy to this land. Now we've got to go on and prove to ourselves that it's worth it."

A shudder ran through Daniel's big frame. He reached for her and pulled her close to him. "There never was another woman like you, Becky."

Daniel Boone and a few other men who were determined not to be pushed out of the wilderness put up cabins on the banks of the Clinch River—as close to *Ken-ta-ke* as they could get—and began to cultivate the land.

In 1773, one of Daniel's neighbors, Judge Richard Henderson, approached him with a startling proposition—the founding of a new colony in Kentucky. It was an ambitious project: Build a road through the wilderness, clear a suitable track of land in the Indian country, survey lots and sell them to settlers under the title of the Transylvania Company. Daniel was awed at the prospect. "You aim to get a grant from the Crown?" he asked.

Henderson smiled. "I don't think we have to worry about the Crown. King George has his hands full up North these days."

"How do you reckon the Injuns are going to like it?"

"I'm prepared to deal with the Indians," Henderson assured him. "I'll buy the land from them. That will be one of your jobs, Boone, to get the Indian leaders together and negotiate with them. I supply the capital, you supply the experience."

Daniel scratched his head. "Well, it might be worth trying."

"Good." Henderson held out his hand, and Daniel took it solemnly. The judge's eyes were bright. "This could make you a rich man, Boone."

Daniel smiled. "I'm as rich now as I ever will be, Judge," he said enigmatically. "But I'll be glad to give you a hand."

In March, 1775, twelve hundred Cherokee chieftains assembled at Sycamore Shoals and signed away twenty million acres of their land to the Transylvania Company for $50,000 in dry goods. On March 10, Daniel Boone, with a crew of thirty men, began the task of clearing the first artery into Kentucky—the Wilderness Road. Swinging axes twelve hours a day, they followed the route of the well-worn Warrior's Trail, widening, clearing brush, and filling in potholes. On April 6, they reach Big Lick on the Kentucky River. Here, at the western terminus of the Wilderness Road, they erected Boonesborough, the capital of Transylvania. Like all settlements in Indian country, Boonesborough consisted of a double row of log cabins laid out in a rectangle with a stockade fence connecting them like the blockhouses of a fort. In September, when the cabins were completed, Daniel went back to Virginia to get his family. Rebecca Boone was the first white woman to set foot west of the Cumberland Mountains.

Meanwhile, other communities were going up in Kentucky. But poor planning and impatience left the new settlers of Transylvania ill-prepared to face the hardships of this wild country. Winter caught them with empty larders, ammunition was low, and the stockades were perilously flimsy and only half completed. In December, Judge Henderson's dreams of empire crumbled as the first news of the Battle of Lexington reached Kentucky.

From the very beginning, the settlers had been disillusioned with the Transylvania Company. They had migrated west to get away from taxation without representation and other injustices inflicted on them by England. But the taxes and other considerable fees levied on them by Richard Henderson were no improvement: Many abandoned the project and went back east. Dissatisfaction was strengthened by fear, as Indian uprisings began to flare up all along the frontier. Operating from their forts on the Mississippi and at Detroit, British agents reopened old wounds. "Every year the Long Knives push you back further and further," they told the Indians. "Soon you will have no hunting grounds." Encouraged by gifts of guns, powder, and war paint, the Shawnee and the Cherokee declared war on the colonists. At Fort Vincennes, British governor Henry Hamilton, "the hair buyer," offered a bounty for American scalps. Only Daniel Boone and a handful of woodsmen stood between the Indians and the British and the exposed flank of the colonies—and their ranks were growing thinner all the time. Richard Henderson was bitter when both the Continental Congress and Virginia Legislature ordered him to dissolve his Transylvania Company.

"It's not fair," he protested to Boone. "It was my money and your sweat that opened up Kentucky."

Daniel was philosophical. "I feel right bad about your money, Mr. Henderson. But my sweat was only a drop in the bucket. Anyhow, they can't rightly take away from us somethin' that wasn't ours to start out with. This land was here long before we were, Mr. Henderson, and I expect it will be here long after us." He grinned. "Besides, I reckon the Congress don't have no choice if they want to save Caintuck from the British."

"How so?" Henderson grumbled.

"A man will fight for land that's his own, but you can't expect him to fight for somethin' that belongs to you, Mr. Henderson."

Ultimately, Kentucky was made a county of Virginia, and Richard Henderson was voted a grant of two hundred thousand acres by the Virginia Legislature in recognition of his contributions to the development of the region.

The new year ushered in a phase in Kentucky history unparalleled for savagery and bloodshed, often referred to as "the seven years of hell." During this time the settlements were under almost constant siege by the Indians. On New Year's Day, 1777, after a week-long siege, the colonists evacuated Mc-Clelland's Station and fled to Boonesborough. Sentries were posted on the walls night and day, and a decree was issued forbidding all but official hunting parties to venture out of the stockade. That spring Daniel Boone was wounded in the ankle in a hand-to-hand skirmish with a Cherokee scouting party only sixty yards from the gate.

In January, 1778, Daniel led a thirty-man detail to Blue Lick Springs to replenish the settlement's salt supply. Making salt was a long and tedious process. Huge iron kettles were filled with the salt-saturated spring water and boiled over log fires until the liquid evaporated, leaving a light crystal crust on the sides of the kettles. A thousand gallons of water yielded a little over a bushel of salt crystal. The operation went smoothly, and within a month they had all but a few of their sacks bulging. Then, one bitter cold morning, Daniel, on a one-man hunting mission, shot a deer at a waterhole near the camp. He slit its throat with his long knife to bleed it, and tied the carcass on his horse's back. Halfway back to camp, he saw a shadow flicker among the trees just off the path. Quickly he reached for his long knife, intending to cut the deer loose and make a run for it. Too late he realized that after he had bled the deer, he had carelessly sheathed his knife without wiping the blade clean. Now, as he tried to draw it, he discovered that the sub-zero cold had frozen the blood, welding it solidly in the sheath. A minute later the path was blocked by Indians.

Daniel was taken to the Shawnee camp a few miles away, where he was received with honor in the wigwam of Chief Blackfish. He learned that Blackfish was preparing to lead a large war party against Boonesborough within the week. Concealing his dismay, Daniel made some rapid calculations. With the thirty men at Blue Lick Springs lost to them, the fighting strength of the garrison was badly impaired. He knew that unless the Shawnees could in some manner be diverted from their purpose, the settlement was doomed. Speaking in Blackfish's own tongue, he said, "I am disappointed. It is said that the great Shawnee chief is a fox. Instead, I find he is clumsy like the bear who charges into the hunters' rifles."

Chief Blackfish scowled darkly. "White chief watch his words. Men's tongues cut out for less."

"I didn't wish to offend," Daniel said humbly. He made a sweeping gesture with his hands. "But surely the Chief is joking when he says he will attack the settlement with this small hunting party.

"I have 125 men," the chief said defensively.

"One hundred twenty-five men!" Daniel choked back his laughter. "There are over 150 men at Boonesborough," he lied, "and they're in a strong fort with plenty of fresh meat and powder and lead to waste." He smiled slyly. "One of your warriors dug the rifle ball out of the deer I shot. Is your powder scarce?"

Chief Blackfish looked embarrassed. "It was a hard winter." He glared suspiciously at Daniel. "But why you tell me this? If you speak true, it will go very bad for us if we attack."

Daniel took a deep breath. The life of Boonesborough, and maybe his own life, depended on his convincing the chief. "Simon Girty and I are old friends," he said with a conspiratorial wink. The name of the sadistic renegade stirred up a murmur among the braves seated in a circle around Chief Blackfish. It was common knowledge that Girty's fanatical hatred of his fellow white men was unmatched by any Indian anywhere.

Chief Blackfish's eyebrows lifted. "You a friend of Simon Girty?"

Daniel nodded. Actually, he had shared an amiable drink with Girty at a local shooting match some years before the renegade's defection. "You want a sign of faith?" Daniel said. "I will give you one. There are thirty white men from Boonesborough at Blue Lick Springs. If I go into their camp and get them to surrender, will you accept me as a brother?"

The chief's black eyes searched Daniel's face. "If this is a trick . . ."

"Then you kill us all," Daniel scoffed. "One hundred and twenty-five warriors don't have to be afraid of thirty white men."

"That is so," the chief admitted soberly.

Daniel launched into the second and most important part of his scheme. "Thirty prisoners should bring a good price from the British Governor at Detroit. You can buy rifles, lead, and powder for a big war against the settlements next spring."

One of the chief's advisors broke in, "That is for the council to decide." Blackfish nodded solemnly. When making important decisions, the Indian nation practiced democracy in its broadest sense. That afternoon, all the braves in Blackfish's war party were summoned to a grand powwow. Daniel's plan was outlined for them and put to a vote. It was approved by a margin of two ballots.

"There is one condition," Daniel told the chief when he was informed of their acceptance. "If I deliver the thirty settlers at Blue Lick Springs into your hands without bloodshed, you must pledge your word that no harm will come to them. You will deliver them alive to Governor Hamilton?"

The chief shrugged. "So be it. Live prisoners bring a better price than scalps in any case. But soon you will be a blood brother of the Shawnee. Why do you concern yourself with these men?"

Daniel met Blackfish's quizzical gaze without flinching. "I kill only for food or to defend myself. Torture I leave for the women and the weaklings."

Blackfish smiled, "I think you are no friend of Simon Girty."

The Shawnees encircled the salt-makers at Blue Lick Springs, and Daniel was sent into the camp to urge their surrender. There were mixed reactions among the woodsmen as he unfolded his plan.

"I never figured you for an Injun lover, Dan'l," one man said with a scowl.

"You sold us out, Boone!" another man said, fingering his long knife.

"Look," Daniel explained patiently but with determination, "the worst it can mean is a British prison camp. You still keep your scalps. The other way, they wipe out Boonesborough. I couldn't let that happen, no matter what."

"And our women and kids," a bearded man echoed. "It means their lives. I'm with Dan'l all the way." Gradually the others were brought around to his viewpoint, although there were several who regarded Boone with sullen resentment as they dropped their arms and waited for the arrival of the Shawnees.

During the long march to Little Chillicothe, the headquarters of the Shawnee nation, some of the white captives were openly rebellious, and there were frequent clashes between individuals of the two factions. After one such exchange, Chief Blackfish informed Daniel that two of the white men would be made to run the gantlet as punishment. Daniel reminded him of his promise that no harm would befall the prisoners. Blackfish pondered over this a minute. It was true he had given *his* word, but under the ancient tribal code, his word was binding on the rest of his braves only as long as they respected his wisdom. Never disposed to treat prisoners too gently, their patience with these white men had reached the limit of its endurance. He knew they were determined to make an example of some of them, even if it meant overriding his authority. It seemed to Blackfish that he must lose face either way. Then the solution came to him. With a thin smile, he looked up at Daniel.

"It is true I gave my word that *they* would not be harmed. Therefore, *you* will run the gantlet." He clasped Daniel's arms. "It is good. Your future brothers will respect your courage and strength."

Daniel's face was pale beneath his tan, but he managed to muster up a weak smile as he stood at the head of a double column of Shawnees and gazed down the long, long corridor between them—120 muscular braves armed with clubs and blunted tomahawks. He filled his lungs with air, and, at a signal from Chief Blackfish, bolted into the gantlet. The Shawnees were completely unprepared for what followed. Instead of running straight down the aisle between the Indians, Daniel zigzagged from side to side, charging head down like a butting ram into the midst of his tormentors, bowling over Indians in twos and threes all down the line. Demoralized by these tactics, most of the Shawnees didn't even lay a club or a tomahawk on him. When he emerged at the other end of the gantlet, he was unmarked, except for a single deep cut over one eye.

Chief Blackfish, who had developed a strong liking for Daniel, was proud of his feat, and the rest of the Shawnees were good-natured about it. The Indians could always appreciate a display of courage or physical prowess, even by an enemy. Those of the white prisoners who had mistrusted Daniel's original motives were sobered by his sacrifice, and from then on the relations between the Indians and the white men were greatly improved.

At Little Chillicothe, Daniel and several other prisoners who resolved to take their chances with the Indians rather than the British were initiated into the Shawnee tribe. In accordance with the custom, they were stripped naked and marched to the river where squaws scrubbed "the white blood" out of them. In a torturous ceremony, their hair was plucked out around a scalp lock on the crown, and finally they were painted and dressed in true Shawnee style. Each man was adopted into an Indian family. As a mark of special esteem, Chief Blackfish made Daniel his son and christened him "Big Turtle."

While the inductees ostensibly were free to come and go as they pleased, actually they were closely supervised. It was always arranged subtly that Daniel never had an opportunity to go hunting alone, even within the limits of the camp; in fact, he was watched by spies. For the first few months, he carefully avoided doing anything that would arouse suspicion. He devoted himself to convincing the Shawnees that he was content in his new role. He threw himself into all their activities with an enthusiasm and vigor designed to put them off guard, and he was successful. A crack shot, he was the most popular attraction at the Indians' shooting matches—but he made sure he lost often enough not to make any enemies. He laughed and joked with the red men, got drunk with them, and even took an Indian wife. And all the time, he watched and waited for the right moment.

His first attempt to escape almost miscarried disastrously. After careful deliberation, he picked the occasion of an overnight hunting expedition to make his break. Because of his extensive knowledge of firearms, Daniel had, early in his Shawnee apprenticeship, been delegated as the gun expert of the tribe. In addition to repairing rifles, his mastery of the delicate procedure of charging the clumsy muzzle-loaders was generally acknowledged—it was said that a rifle which "Big Turtle" loaded always shot straighter. Before the hunters broke camp, Daniel sat down to his customary duties with the guns. None of the braves suspected he was palming the balls which he appeared to be dropping into the rifle barrels and was slipping them into a pouch at his waist. His original plan called for him to make a break for freedom later in the morning as they approached a wide river. He was a powerful underwater swimmer and felt that water offered his best avenue of escape.

Unhappily, a deer upset his timetable by freezing on the trail shortly after they had started out. The brave nearest the animal threw his rifle to his shoulder and fired at a range of about ten yards. Obviously unhurt, the deer streaked off into the forest. The startled Indian blinked, looked down at his rifle, and stared at Daniel accusingly. There was an alarming moment of silence as all eyes turned slowly in his direction. Daniel knew that even if he could dismiss the phenomenon of a pointblank miss, once the brave who had fired the shot began to think, his recollection of the light recoil would give away the ruse.

The split-second response of mind and muscle that had so often saved his life did not desert him now. Leaping high into the air like a madman, he began to shout: "Abracadabra puddin' an' pie. 'Big Turtle' heap big medicine man!" Before the Indians could recover from their amazement, he started to run away down the path. He hadn't covered twenty yards when a dozen guns blazed away. Stopping suddenly, he whipped off his buckskin cloak and flourished it in front of him. With a big grin, he shook a hail of rifle balls out of the cloak onto the ground. The Indians gathered around him and examined the bullets dubiously. "See," Daniel said quickly, waving his cloak around, "magic skin stops bullets." He sank down on the ground and began to laugh, hugging himself and shaking his head at the dumbfounded Indians. Suddenly a grin stole across the face of one brave. " 'Big Turtle' no medicine man. 'Big Turtle' make a big joke."

Other Shawnees began to smile sheepishly; they had a weakness for jokes. Daniel went limp with relief as the laughter was picked up all around.

Ironically, his eventual escape was accomplished strictly on impulse. Daniel was out with another hunting party on a June morning when a strange whirring sound in the distance brought them up short. Minutes later, the sky was blotted out and a great rush of wind rustled the leaves of the trees. He looked up at the biggest flock of wild turkeys he had ever seen. In their excitement, the Shawnees could think of nothing else but that they must have some of the big birds for their holiday feasts. Scattering into the forest in the wake of the turkeys, they left him alone for the first time since his capture. Without hesitation, he started to run in the opposite direction.

The Shawnees weren't long in realizing their error. Within a quarter of an hour, a posse was on his trail. As he sprinted eastward, Daniel knew the advantage was all with the Indians. His short headstart was more than offset by the Shawnees' familiarity with this section of the country. This was presently confirmed when he came up short at the brink of a precipice that fell off a sheer fifty feet to the valley floor. As he stood on the edge of the drop and heard the angry war cries and crashing of underbrush closing in behind him, his hopes went spiraling down. Desperately, his eyes swept the valley beneath him. About twenty feet away and about fifteen feet below him, the tip of a tall pine tree swayed leisurely in the breeze. His jaw thrust out and his mouth tightened. He backed up until his back touched the forest. He took a deep breath and began to run toward the rim of the cliff. He leaped out into space, crouched low like a broad jumper, with his hands reaching out in front of him. Feet first, he plunged into the cushion of pine needles, feeling the branches tear at his flesh as he went hurtling down through them. Eyes shut tight, arms held high for protection, he clawed wildly to stop his descent. The breath was pinched out of him as his body smashed into something solid. Instinctively, his arms closed in a bear hug around the trunk of the tree. He held on desperately as the slender, flexible tip of the pine snapped, swayed, and finally held steady beneath his weight. Then he slid to the ground and limped away into the forest—sore and bruised, but safe. Four days later, he staggered through the gate of Boonesborough—160 miles away—looking like a drunken Indian. "The Shawnee are comin'," he gasped, and then collapsed.

The next morning, despite the ordeal he had been through, Daniel was up and about, directing the feverish preparations to meet the Indian threat. Rebecca had long since given him up for dead and had gone back to Virginia with her family, a fact for which Daniel was grateful under the circumstances. However, his daughter, Jemima, and her husband, Flanders

Callaway, were still in Boonesborough, as was his brother Squire.

Daniel was shocked by the rundown condition of the settlement. "You folks must be daft!" he complained bitterly to Major Smith, an army officer who had been sent from Virginia to govern the settlement in his absence. "Look at that stockade. She's sagging like a swayback mule. Whole sections of it are rottin' away."

The major reddened. "Things have been so quiet this year, I guess we didn't give it much thought."

Daniel clapped a hand to his head. "Sittin' smack in the middle of Shawnee country and you let your fort go to pot. How are you on powder and lead?"

"Rock bottom." The major's color deepened.

"And manpower?"

"About thirty men and maybe twenty boys who can handle a rifle."

Daniel groaned. "And nine hundred running feet of fence to protect." He buried his face in his hands. "Lordy, I danced the Injuns' tune all winter to save this place. I might as well have saved myself the trouble and humiliation, it looks like."

But the peril confronting them didn't give Daniel much time to brood. That morning mounted messengers rode out of Boonesborough to Virginia and to the other settlements in Kentucky, seeking reinforcements and supplies. All hands—men, women, and children—went to work repairing and strengthening the stockade. Hunters tramped the woods around the clock to fill the depleted larders. Every available container was filled with water, and several wells were started in the courtyard.

The messengers returned. The other Kentucky settlements sent their regrets to Boonesborough, but that was all; they had neither powder, lead, nor men to spare. Still, Daniel breathed easier as two months passed without any sign of Indians. "We're as ready for 'em now as we ever will be," he said. "And any day now the governor's reinforcements will be along." But there was no help from Virginia, either, and early in September the Shawnees arrived.

It was just before noon on a dry, hot morning that the sentries stationed on strategic hilltops around the fort galloped through the gates with the long dreaded news. "The redskins are comin'!" Daniel had drilled the colonists tirelessly for this moment, and immediately the well-oiled machinery of defense went into motion. The men and boys took their posts at the portholes, and the women set up their reloading stations on the ground behind them. A number of the huskier girls dressed up in men's clothing in order to mislead any Shawnee scouts who might be spying on the stockade from distant treetops. Within the hour, Boonesborough was encircled and the siege was under way.

In the first phase of the battle, the attackers subjected the stockade to a steady barrage of rifle fire. Listening to the balls splattering against the sturdy logs, Daniel grinned. "Lucky we mended that fence or just the wind from all that flying lead would blow it down." All afternoon, he kept moving among the defenders, shouting suggestions and words of encouragement above the roar of gunfire. "Don't shoot 'less you have a target. We gotta make every shot count. Keep low," he told the men at the portholes. "Don't give 'em no more than an eyeball to fix on."

That night the Indians tried a sneak raid on the fence. By torchlight, the colonists beat them off with heavy losses. But there was little sleep to be gotten in Boonesborough that night. Daniel dozed off just before dawn, only to be awakened in a half-hour by his daughter Jemima, who was on the verge of hysteria. "Daddy, Daddy, come quick! They set the fence afire!" He ran outside and crossed the courtyard to the north wall, where a crowd of men had gathered. Earlier in the year, the settlers had started to build a corral on this side of the stockade, but the project had been abandoned after one section was completed. This section, set at right angles to the main fence, ran off almost to the edge of the woods. When Daniel came up, Squire told him excitedly, "Them divils set fire to that old fence. With the wind blowin' this way, it won't be an hour before it creeps up to the stockade."

Daniel looked grim. "There's only one way to stop it. We gotta rip down that fence where it touches the stockade."

"But how?" Major Smith asked. "It would be murder to send men over the wall into that gunfire."

Daniel tilted his high hat back on his head. "That ain't what I had in mind, Major. I figgered on goin' under it."

At his direction, a detail of men dug a tunnel under the stockade. Breaking through the surface beneath the burning fence, they were able to pull down the pickets and pass them back through the tunnel without exposing themselves to the Shawnee snipers. When a safe gap had been cleared in the fence, they filled in the tunnel again.

Unwilling to give up the idea of setting fire to Boonesborough, the Indians lobbed a diabolically ingenious kind of fire-bomb over the walls. The bomb consisted of a hollowed-out arrow backed with gunpowder and a time fuse made out of punk. Most of the bombs were duds because of the unreliability of the punk fuse, but those that did explode caused some serious fires which drained heavily on the settlement's precious water supply and constantly harassed the weary defenders. One morning it was observed that the nearby Kentucky River was brown with mud near the shoreline. As the day wore on, the concentration of silt swirling past in the current became heavier and heavier. Daniel was more concerned than he had been since the siege began. "Looks to me like they aim to tunnel under us," he told the men. "Surprise us some night."

"What can we do, Dan'l?" Squire demanded.

"Nothin', 'less we know where the tunnel lays." He kicked at the dirt helplessly. "Them fire-bombs and now this. They ain't Injun tricks. I smell the English behind it." As a single black cloud scudded across the sun, he looked up at the sky. "The only hope we got is up there."

As if to divert attention from their latest project, the Shawnees stepped up their assaults on the walls. Squire Boone had the inspiration to burn out the center of a gum log that was too tough to cut up for firewood and fashion a cannon out of it. The settlers effectively baffled the Indians with the makeshift artillery until the log blew up in their faces and badly injured the gun crew.

On the night of September 17, it began to rain, a heavy, wind-whipped downpour that penetrated the crevices of the log cabins and saturated everything. Shivering and soaked to the skin, the sentries on the wall whispered to one another in the wet blackness. Daniel slapped the pickets happily. "Won't have to fret about fire for a while, anyhow. These logs won't dry out for at least a week." Day came bright and beautiful, the sunlight shimmering in rainbows through the sodden leaves. With the light, a cheer went up from the east side of the stockade. From a clump of trees at the edge of the river, a deep trench extended across the clearing to a point about five feet from the perimeter of the picket fence. Daniel grabbed his daughter Jemima and danced a little jig in the mud. "And that's the end of their tunnel," he laughed. "That rain collapsed it."

That afternoon the bedraggled Shawnee Army withdrew from Boonesborough and started the long trek west. The failure of their tunnel was only one of many factors that brought about the withdrawal; casualties in the nine-day siege had been heavy, and they were beginning to feel the pinch in powder and lead caused by early extravagances. The settlers realized the measure of this extravagance when they salvaged 125 pounds of lead from the stockade.

After the successful defense of Boonesborough, Daniel joined his family in Yadkin Valley. In 1779, they returned to Kentucky to find that, in the interval, things had quieted down. Reverses in the East had forced the British to curtail their aid to the Indians. Boonesborough was enjoying a welcome holiday from war. Migration had picked up from the East; new settlements were springing up; and the old ones were expanding. The expansion made Daniel restless.

"You're getting that feelin' again, ain't you, Dan'l?" Rebecca asked him one night. "I can tell."

He squirmed uncomfortably under her shrewd eyes. "When I look around and see all these cabins and people, I feel like

I'm smotherin'. This place is gettin' too civilized for me. I need elbow room, Becky."

"I understand, Dan'l," she said.

Daniel stayed in Boonesborough a few months longer; then he built a sturdy, barricaded cabin in the woods about five miles from the settlement and moved into it with his family.

One day in October, a Shawnee raiding party caught Daniel unarmed in his tobacco shed. He was standing on a ladder inspecting some leaves that were drying on a tier near the roof when four braves slunk through the door. With his usual presence of mind, Daniel greeted them pleasantly, and even after the leader informed him that they were going to take him prisoner, he made no fuss.

"I'd like to make you a present of some fine tobacco," he told the Indians. "Here. Gather 'round and I'll hand it down to you."

Daniel was well aware that tobacco had to be handled with extreme caution, and that at any violent disturbance, the dry, powdery leaves would kick up a snuff storm. As the Indians moved in obediently around the foot of the ladder, he got a firm hold on a stack of leaves and yanked hard. "Here you are, boys, ketch!" He hurled the tobacco down on top of them, and, while the poor braves staggered blindly about the shed, sneezing, coughing, and cursing, he escaped through the door.

To Daniel's amazement, new settlers flocking in from the East and North hailed him as a national hero. During the war years, his name had become a legend in the colonies. By popular demand he was honored with a seat in the Kentucky assembly. Quite unexpectedly, too, his vast tracts of land promised to make him a rich man. Real estate was a booming business in the rapidly growing state. But Daniel was anything but happy. "I ain't no lawmaker," he told Becky. "I'm a woodsman. Sittin' through one of them law-makin' sessions is worse than runnin' the gantlet."

"Quit then," his wife said. "It ain't like we needed the

money. Why, that real estate feller who was here last week said you'd be a millionaire if you'd sell your property."

"No!" Daniel was vehement. They're not goin' to ruin my land. They knock down the trees, kill all the livin' things, cut the land up in little pieces, and put it all behind fences. Lord, before you know it, a man ain't got no room to flex his muscles."

But the tide of progress was not to be stemmed by one man. Unscrupulous land speculators in Virginia discovered that Daniel had never filed proper claims on his property, and they gobbled it up anyway. He appealed to the courts, but even his most influential friends in the government shook their heads hopelessly. "They got the law on their side," they said. "How could you have been so neglectful about filing claims?"

"Claims?" Daniel said uncomprehendingly. "I found that land. I fought for it. My blood and sweat are in that soil. What more claim can a man have?" Still he accepted his defeat philosophically. "It don't really matter none," he told his family. "Soon this land will be dead for me anyways, the way it's bein' strangled by civilization."

During the next decade, he kept moving just ahead of the creeping frontier, keeping to the woods where he could hunt and fish and be near the things he loved. In 1789 the Spanish government, in view of his contributions to the colonization of Kentucky, invited him to their Missouri territory with the promise of a big land grant. Daniel jumped at the offer, chiefly because he couldn't resist the lure of a strange frontier.

The next thirty years were the most satisfying of his entire life. The land was wild and open in Missouri. Hunting was good, and the soil was rich for farming. There was plenty of room between neighbors. In 1803, the territory passed under the jurisdiction of the United States as a part of the Louisiana Purchase, and Daniel's land was taken from him again.

"What are you goin' to do about it?" his friends asked him angrily.

Daniel just grinned. "Goin' huntin', that's what I'm gonna

do." A few years later, Congress granted him one thousand acres of land as a token of "his many eminent services." Daniel promptly sold it, paid off his debts, and moved his family further out into the wilderness.

After Rebecca died in 1813, the old restlessness came over him again, stronger than it had been in years. His children, all grown and married, begged him to give up his lonely cabin in the forest and to come and live with one of them. Daniel was horrified at the prospect.

On September 26, 1820, he died at the age of eighty-six. His sons buried him on a high hill overlooking the Missouri River. Daniel would have liked that. There was plenty of elbow room.

Simon Kenton's War with the Indians

By CHARLES HEWES

*Eight times the Shawnees made Simon run the dreaded gant-
let; they even tried to burn him at the stake. And still they
couldn't break his body or his spirit.*

Simon Kenton stumbled down the trail in the half-light of
early morning. Every inch of his six-foot-one body ached and
was thick with stiffness, but the Shawnee braves shoved him
on toward the village. A half-hour of walking gradually re-
stored the circulation to his legs, which had been tightly
bound the night before. Then an Indian grabbed his shoulder
and twisted him around.

"We stop here!" the Shawnee said. "Sit down!" He turned
to another brave in the war party. "Run to the village," he
ordered. "Tell them we hold the red-haired Long Knife

prisoner!" The brave sprinted lightly along the trail while the other Indians gathered in a circle around the white scout and stared at him curiously. Kenton looked coldly past them into the forest and waited. Suddenly the war whoops of hundreds of Indians echoed through the woods.

"Now you will face our people in the village," the leader said. "Get to your feet, old woman!" He prodded Simon with his tomahawk. The trail broadened for a quarter mile, and then the forest fell away and they stood before the village of Chillicothe. It was a large village with many lodges walled with bark; in the center stood the long council house. But the scout saw none of this. The moment he stepped into the clearing he was faced with four hundred maddened Shawnees. Every man, woman, and boy in the village had drawn up in two lines facing each other about six feet apart. Some held tomahawks, but most had clubs to beat the white man when he ran the gantlet. Naked youngsters, too young to join the sport, stood behind their elders and stared at the white man. A tall, older Indian whose hair was streaked with white walked up to him. There was no mistaking the man—he was Chief Blackfish. The scout sucked in his cheeks. Blackfish's favorite hobby was taking the scalps of women and children.

"You are Simon Kenton," he said bitterly. "You have fought the Shawnee with Daniel Boone. That is your misfortune. Now my people will have their revenge." Simon glanced at the two rows of Indians. An old hag with a switch lined with thorns headed one, and an ancient brave swinging a club headed the other. "Prepare yourself," Blackfish continued. "My people will soon know whether your blood is the color of your hair or as pale as your face." As he spoke, the wrinkled old hag sprang forward and whipped her switch at Simon's face. He threw up an arm to stop the blow, and the thorns slashed through his flesh. Before she could strike again, one of the braves roughly pushed her back into line. Then Blackfish raised his arm, and a heavy drum boomed through the village. It was the signal for Simon to run the gantlet. He sucked air into his lungs three times and then felt a knife dig a quarter inch into his back over his left kidney.

"Run, you dog!" the brave behind him snarled. In desperation, Simon sprinted forward. But he didn't get by the old Indian at the head of the line. The old man's club caught him on the shoulder and knocked him against the Shawnees in the other line. Simon spun around twice and then saw his chance. He raced down the gantlet hugging one line of Indians. Those he brushed against were too close to put strength into the blows they aimed at him, and those on the other side couldn't swing freely without the risk of landing a blow on one of their neighbors. Simon covered half the gantlet without taking a solid blow and was sure he could go the distance. Then he saw the flash of a sharply-honed tomahawk twenty feet ahead. One brave had stepped out of line and was blocking his way. Simon quickly ran his eyes up and down the two lines. Two twelve-year-old boys were guarding the spot he hoped to break through. They saw him coming but couldn't hold him back. It was a second or two before the Indians realized that he had broken out of the gantlet and raced after him. He stopped dead, swiveled, and swerved in a beautiful exhibition of broken-field running. The Shawnees lunged and swung at him, but he was an elusive target, and he slowly made his way toward the council house.

"Circle him! Circle him!" Blackfish cried. The braves tried, but they were too late. He had already broken into the clear and was running for the council house. Hard on his heels came the villagers shrieking in frustration. Once he tripped, but he rolled to his feet and kept on running. Clenching his teeth, Simon put on a final burst of speed. He threw himself through the door of the council house and fell gasping to the ground. The howling Shawnees pulled up to a halt outside. They hurled curses in after him, but no one dared to enter. A prisoner who ran the gantlet and reached the council house was protected by an ancient, almost sacred, law. No one could touch him until the council met and determined his fate.

But even as he lay panting on the ground, Simon knew he had only postponed the inevitable. The best he could hope for would be a quick death rather than long, drawn-out torture at the stake. His mouth twisted in an ironic grin. It might have been better after all if the authorities in Virginia had hanged him for murder.

Simon Kenton was born in western Virginia on a brisk morning early in April, 1755. Mary Kenton had been expecting the birth for almost a month, and the women in the town had hovered around her. This was a special event—her seventh child. Everyone knew that seventh children—especially boys—were marked from birth by extraordinary powers. Outside the cabin, Mark Kenton shared a jug with several of his neighbors, and when they heard the baby's first lusty howl, they knew it was a boy. Then they proceeded to get roundly drunk.

To people in the wilderness, every healthy son was a potential breadwinner who could help carry the heavy burden of life. But as Simon grew up, he didn't see it that way. He was a seventh child and he was different all right—the only burden he ever carried was his own sturdy frame, and he hated to do even that. He was lazy to the core, although he did excel at two things. First, he grew—he shot up to over six feet; and second, no one could match his skill at avoiding a chore by slipping out of sight into the woods.

When he was sixteen, Simon fell madly in love. The girl's name was Ellen Cummins, and the fact that she was a year older than he didn't matter a bit to him. He aimed to marry her and he set about courting her, but it wasn't easy. Ellen was a real beauty with a firmly rounded figure, jet black hair, and eyes that sparkled at every handsome boy in the village. She was a prize worth fighting for, and Simon soon whipped all his rivals but one, a man in his twenties named William Leachman. Everyone in the village knew that Ellen was going to choose between them, and Simon openly boasted to his friends that she would soon be his. He was banking on the way she responded to his artlessly violent love-making.

But Ellen was wise. Simon was still a good-natured, happy-go-lucky youngster, while William Leachman was a serious-minded young man and a hard worker. He would be able to give her a home to be proud of. One night at a dance, Ellen took Simon aside. "Simon," she said in a warm, soft voice, "you're a fine, handsome lad, but you won't be settling down to hard work for years—maybe never, for all I know—and I want to have children and look after them right." She paused and looked him square in the eye. "I told William that I'd marry him."

Simon took it hard. It was a bitter blow to his pride. And he had wanted her fiercely.

Ellen Cummins and William Leachman were married in grand style, and almost the entire village gathered at the Cummins' house for the party that followed the wedding. Simon wasn't invited, but no one was surprised when he came swaggering into the gathering. They were surprised, however, when he suddenly scooped the bride up in his arms and bolted for the door. He might have made it too, if one of the groom's brothers hadn't picked that moment to come through the same door. Ellen was quickly returned to her family, and Simon was escorted outside by William Leachman and two of his brothers.

"Don't you waste no time with him, Will," John Leachman said. "Just take my rifle and put a ball through his heart." Mixing with another man's wife was a risky business. Usually, the husband shot the man on the spot and the other men in the village thanked him for his trouble.

"He ain't no more than a boy," Leachman said. "I reckon I'll just beat the living daylights out of him. Might be it'll teach him to mind his manners." The fight was a corker, and one by one the men and women inside the house drifted out to watch. Fighting was born into the people on the frontier, and a good fist fight was worth watching. There were no rules, and no holds were barred. When a man went down, he could expect a kick in the face, or if the fighting was at close quarters, a finger in the eye or a knee in the groin. Back and forth the two men slugged, butted, and kicked. Time and again they threw each other to the ground. Simon was fighting savagely, wildly determined to heal the hurt to his pride. Leachman fought just as fiercely to avenge the insult to his wife. In the end, Leachman's age and weight told; he gave

Simon the beating of his life. When he staggered to his feet, Simon's face and body were raw with cuts. But the wounds didn't hurt nearly so much as the thought of being whipped in front of Ellen and her neighbors. He was jeered off the farm. He had come looking for a fight and William Leachman had beaten the hell out of him. It was exactly what he deserved.

But Simon wasn't through. He was determined to fight Leachman again and whip him. He took his time and waited till one day when he saw Leachman enter the woods to cut boards for his new house—the one Ellen would live in. Simon flushed in anger. "Hold up and fight!" he shouted. The other man spun around and met Simon's maddened charge. The fight was a repeat of the first. They slugged and butted, and Leachman's weight began to wear Simon down. In desperation, Simon shoved the heavier man backwards into a tree. Then, he caught the thong which tied Leachman's long hair behind his head and hooked it on a low hanging branch. When Simon let go of the branch, Leachman's head snapped back, exposing his chin. Simon planted a hard right on it. Then, in a fury of revenge, he poured on one blow after another. Leachman was soon knocked senseless, but Simon continued to punch till his arms were tired. Suddenly he realized that Leachman was hanging limply from the branch by his hair; his face was raw, and blood poured from his mouth and nose.

"Good God!" Simon gasped. "I've killed him!" That was more than he had bargained for, and he ran into the woods. Murderers weren't given a second chance in those days. They were simply strung up to the nearest tree without benefit of trial. That night, Simon fled west toward Kentucky. The next day he hid, and it wasn't until the fourth day of his flight that he stopped at a cabin and asked for food.

After a week, he began to travel during the day and stop at cabins for the night. At one of them he met a man named Butler. After eating supper and swapping a few yarns in front of the fire, Butler turned to the boy. "Seems like you could use some new clothes," he said. "Tell you what. I could use a hand to help me out with the hoeing. If you see fit, the job's yours, and I'll stake you to a new outfit." He watched the indecision on Simon's face. "If you're planning to be going farther west," he added, "you're agoing to need a rifle. I have one that'll suit you just right." That settled the matter. Simon had never owned a rifle, and he wanted one badly. For the first time in his life, he worked hard. The promised rifle was too great a prize to lose.

One evening when he and Butler were headed back to the cabin after a long day in the field, Butler said. "Simon, the hoeing is done and you did a man's share of the work. I reckon you've earned your new clothes and that rifle I promised you." The next morning, Simon hefted his new rifle, said good-bye to his friend, and headed west again. But now there was a difference. He had a new spring in his step. He had earned his clothing and rifle fair and square, and now he could earn himself a reputation as a woodsman. Still, there was that murder hanging over his head, so to confuse anyone who might follow him, he changed his last name to Butler in honor of his friend, "Cousin Butler."

For the next few years, Simon hunted and trapped with two other men. Then he felt able to go it alone. He had learned to slip through the woods like an Indian, and now he was full grown, 195 hard-muscled pounds on a six-foot, one-inch frame. It didn't matter to him that Kentucky was the hunting and fighting ground of a dozen different Indian tribes. If he met one or two braves, he would stand and fight. If there were more, he would turn and run them into the ground.

Late one summer afternoon, Simon headed back to his camp, sweating under a load of pelts and game. He had been out since dawn and he was dead on his feet. All he wanted to do was flop down in his sack and sleep. He was about to walk straight into camp, but then he stopped. He was hunting alone now, and he would never have a chance to make more than one mistake. He hid his furs and made a wide circle around his campsite. The second time around, he came up in back of a Shawnee brave hiding at the edge of the camp. Quietly Simon drew back his tomahawk and drove it into the back of the Indian's head. He caught the body and eased it to the ground without a sound. A few deft cuts with his knife gained him the brave's scalping lock. Then he continued on his cautious way and found a second brave. This one lost his scalp too. Then, satisfied that there were no more Indians about, he retrieved his furs and settled down to a watchful night.

The next morning, Simon saw signs of many war parties. That was enough for him. He packed everything he could carry and drifted back east to Fort Pitt, where he met his friend George Rogers Clark, who was a couple of years older than Simon and was also a six-footer with a mass of flaming red hair. "We're heading for an all-out war with the Indians," Clark told Simon. "They've been asking for it, and we're going to give it to them." Young Shawnee and Cherokee braves had been raiding isolated cabins for years. "We're going to push them back across the Ohio River," Clark said, "and we've got the men to do it—two divisions of the Virginia Army and fifteen hundred militiamen."

"What about the Delawares and Mingos?" Simon asked.

"The way the men look at it, there are no friendly Indians. Either they clear out or get killed."

"Well, now," Simon said, "I've made some pretty good friends among the Mingos in the past couple of years."

"Don't test their friendship now," Clark said. "Some of the boys have been raiding Indian style and bringing back scalps. Do you know Logan?"

Everyone knew John Logan, the chief of the Mingos. He spoke English and French and liked the whites so much he had taken one of their names.

"A while back," Clark said, "Logan's brother and sister and a couple of dozen other Mingos were murdered by a band of crazy whites. Logan sent a letter declaring war. He's already taken thirty scalps and swears that's just the beginning." Clark paused. "I've signed up as a scout. Why don't you join me?"

Simon hesitated. Clark was a good army man, but he

wasn't much of a scout. "Who else you got to scout with you?" he asked.

Clark clapped his hands together and grinned. "I've got a real catch, Simon Girty!"

"Never heard of him."

"Hell, man! He knows more about the damn redskins than any white man alive. He was captured by the Senecas and lived with them for three years." Clark slapped Simon on the back. "Come on! It's time you met Girty over a jug of good whiskey. He's the interpreter here at the fort."

Simon was instantly struck by Girty's appearance. He was a short, thick-set man whose round face sat square on his shoulders. Dark eyes full of sadness dominated his face. For eighteen years he had lived as naturally with the Indians as he had with the whites, and it was a hard choice to fight them.

The army marched into Indian territory in two forces. The first was made up of Governor Dunmore's two divisions of Virginia Infantry. They marched in sharply formed ranks like good soldiers. The second group was the militia under General Lewis. They were backwoodsmen and skulked through the forest like a giant Indian war party. The commanding officers were as different from each other as their forces were. Dunmore marched boldly ahead looking for Indians. Lewis moved cautiously and avoided showing the Indians his strength. They were soon arguing with one another about how to fight the war, and the three scouts had to carry silly dispatches back and forth through the Indian lines every day.

On one of their dashes through the Indian lines, Clark fell behind Simon and Girty. He cursed his bad luck and stumbled along, trusting that luck would keep him on the right trail and hoping that his friends would soon be back for him. Then he heard welcome words.

"Clark! Over here, Clark! Come on!"

"Hey!" Clark called back. "Over here!"

When he heard Clark's name being called, Girty, who was a few feet ahead of Simon, spun around. The two experienced woodsmen raced silently back through the forest. As they broke into a clearing, they saw Clark with his back toward them. Behind him were two Indians with upraised tomahawks. Without a word, the two woodsmen whipped out their own tomahawks and threw them hard; they couldn't risk the noise of a shot. Before the braves could strike, razor-sharp tomahawks had split their skulls. As they fell to the ground, Clark spun around, raising his rifle.

"What the hell!" Then he saw the two dead Shawnees.

Simon and Girty bent to pick up their tomahawks. "You were just about taken in by the oldest Indian trick going," Simon said to Clark. "It's real cute. One of the braves will sneak up close to a camp and listen for one man to call another by name. Then he slips back to his war party, and they set up an ambush. Most of the time it works!" He snapped his fingers and grinned broadly. Even Girty's sad eyes smiled.

Clark's face turned the color of his flaming red hair. "Let's get the hell out of here and deliver that message from Dunmore!" he snapped.

General Lewis of the militia swore up and down and sideways when he read the message the scouts delivered. "That damn fool Dunmore wants us to join his army," he growled. "Didn't you scouts report that there are war parties already behind his lines?" The scouts nodded. "Well I'm not joining him! We're staying here and waiting for them red men."

Fifteen hundred braves attacked the militia the next morning. The battle between the evenly-matched forces seesawed back and forth for seven hours. Then the Indians broke off the fight and slipped back into the forest. Lewis and the scouts breathed a sigh of relief. Their army had taken 300 casualties, the enemy only 150. But that was enough. The Indians were always sensible about fighting, and if their losses were too great, they would simply pull back and attack some other day. This time they pulled way back, across the Ohio River, and the next morning the chiefs sent a message under a flag of truce. They wanted to speak with Dunmore and Lewis about a peace treaty. Only John Logan, the Mingo chief, refused to attend the council meeting. He sent a message saying that he would abide by the treaty, but that he would never forgive the murderers of his family. Most of the white men sympathized with him, and when Simon personally visited the chief and expressed his regrets, they became great friends.

Meanwhile, the chiefs promised to keep their young braves from raiding in Virginia and Pennsylvania. The militia was disbanded. They packed up and rode for home, and Simon returned to hunting and trapping in the forests of Kentucky.

The braves of two dozen different tribes had always considered Kentucky their personal hunting grounds. Now the whites were moving in and destroying all the game. This was a danger to all the tribes, and they banded together to strike at the settlers. Many travelers were ambushed and scalped until Simon Kenton—or Simon Butler as he still called himself—volunteered to scout for them. The settlers placed their lives in the hands of this big, friendly youngster who was not yet twenty-one, and he served them well. Not a single person was lost from the dozens of parties he led to the forts and villages in Kentucky.

When war broke out between the thirteen colonies and England, Simon was neutral, until the English began using the Indians the same way the French had used them a few years before. Then he knew for whom he had to fight. He joined Daniel Boone at Boonesborough and became his chief scout. During the long winter, he slipped out of the fort day after day and brought back game for the starving settlers inside. Only a few brave men left the security of the forts that winter, and many of them didn't come back. Indians were everywhere.

One brisk April morning shortly after dawn, Simon joined two men at the stockade gate. Casually, he swung his eyes over the clearing between the fort and the forest and suddenly tensed. "Sound the alarm!" he ordered. "We're in for trouble!"

"Indians?" one of the men asked. Simon nodded. "Goddamn it, Simon," the man said, "I've been standing here since the sun came up and I ain't seen a sign of 'em. What do you do, smell 'em out?"

"Look at the cows." Simon pointed down the lane. "They were turned out to pasture at dawn, but instead of heading for the open fields and gorging themselves on sweet grass, they're milling around and sniffing the air. Keep your eyes on 'Old Spot.' She can sniff an Indian a half mile away." Even as they watched, "Old Spot" turned and started waddling back to the fort with the other cows trailing meekly behind her.

"Jessup and Higgins are out hunting," one man said. "They're walking right into a trap."

"Get your rifles ready," Simon snapped, "and follow me. They're going to need all the help we can give 'em." Simon led the men out of the fort, but they hadn't covered more than a dozen paces when Jessup and Higgins burst out of the woods ahead of them. On their heels came six Shawnees with rifles. One of the warriors stopped, lifted his rifle, and fired. Higgins jerked to one side, stumbled, and fell forward on his face. Another Shawnee leaped at the fallen man. Simon raised his rifle and fired. The brave straightened up and stared silently at the fort. Then, the knife slipped from his hand, and he twisted and fell to the ground. The two men with Simon fired, and another brave fell. The four remaining Shawnees stopped their charge for a moment; that was all the time Jessup needed to reach the party from the fort.

"How many of them are there?" Simon asked as he reloaded his rifle.

"Don't know," Jessup gasped. "Them six were all we saw."

Once again the braves charged the men reloading their rifles. As they did, Daniel Boone came racing out of the fort with a dozen men at his heels. The Indians fired hurriedly and ran for the forest. Boone's men let go a volley and went after them; the whites wanted all the scalps they could get.

"Stop!" Simon shouted. "Stop! It's a trap!" At this moment, one hundred screaming braves rushed out of the woods and ran to cut the men off from the fort.

"It's Blackfish!" Daniel Boone said. "Back to the fort! Hurry!" The settlers ran, but they weren't fast enough to prevent ten speedy Shawnees from getting between them and the fort.

"We've got a fight on our hands, boys!" Boone cried. "Sell your lives as dear as possible!" They were still sixty yards from the fort when Simon saw that one of the braves had Boone lined up in the sights of his rifle. He swung his heavy, long rifle up to his shoulder and fired. The Indian fell, and Simon had chalked up two scores with two shots that morning. As he ran, he shook powder from his horn into the rifle. He rammed it down and spit a lead ball out of his mouth into the barrel; it was a trick he had learned while hunting by himself on the frontier. He looked for a target and found one quickly. Boone's ankle had been shattered by an Indian shot, and he sat on the ground, fighting off another brave who was after his scalp. Simon's third shot killed his third Indian.

"Turn and pour it into 'em!" he shouted to the men, as he ran to help Boone.

Boone was fighting hand to hand from a sitting position with still another Shawnee. Simon swung his long rifle and had the satisfaction of seeing the heavy iron barrel split open the brave's head. Then he scooped Boone up and threw him over his shoulder. It was a hard run to the safety of the fort, but he made it. So did the others.

Except for Boone, none of them had even received a serious wound. They had a whale of a battle the rest of the day, but when night fell, the Shawnees pulled back and disappeared.

After the fight was over, Boone called Simon to his cabin. "It's good to see you, boy," he said. "I don't like to talk much, but I want to say that you acted like a man today—as fine a fellow as I'd want to know." Simon thanked him. This was high praise for a boy who had a murder rap hanging over his head.

In the late spring of 1778, Simon went east to round up men to fight in Kentucky. At Fort Pitt, he found that his friend George Rogers Clark had been commissioned a major and already had an army. "You wouldn't be thinking of taking your army out without me, would you?" Simon asked Clark.

"You're my scout from now until we take Kaskaskia," Clark roared slapping him on the back.

"What about Girty?" Simon asked. "He scouting for you too?"

Clark's blue eyes went steel cold. "You haven't heard about Girty," he said. "He's gone back to the Indians."

"I thought he was commissioned a captain in the militia," Simon said.

"The orders never came through," Clark said sadly. "I guess that's why he's gone back to their side. The Shawnees made him a chief." Simon was bitterly disappointed. He had liked Girty from the start.

Clark's little army swept through the Midwest, taking one British outpost after another. When it had taken Kaskaskia, Simon turned and went back to Kentucky with the news. He was just in time to go scouting for acting governor Bowman. Simon, someone named Montgomery, and a short fat man named George took off into the woods to reconnoiter the Indian village of Chillicothe.

"Bowman isn't about to take this village," Simon said. "He hasn't got the men. I reckon we'd better get back and put the facts before him before he does something foolish!"

Montgomery frowned. "It don't seem right that we should go back empty-handed after coming all this distance. I've seen where they keep the horses corraled. What do you say we take a few?"

"The town's swarming with braves," Simon said. "We'd better just get the hell out of here."

"I'm with Montgomery," George said eagerly, caught up by the humor and adventure of stealing horses from the Indians—horse-stealing had been an Indian monopoly. Simon was outvoted, but he didn't mind. This was the lighthearted kind of escapade that he liked anyway. The three men crawled down to the corral, baited some horses with handfuls of salt, and threw halters over their heads. When they charged out of the corral, every brave in the village heard the thunder of horses' hooves.

"Long Knives!" the Indians shouted. "Long Knives! The

horses!" At once every brave in the village was on his feet and running. But the hard-riding whites quickly disappeared in the brush. When they had put a half dozen miles between themselves and the village, they stopped to catch their breath.

"Say, this was a real haul," Montgomery said gleefully as he looked over the horses they had stolen from the Indians. "Wait till they hear about this back at the fort!"

"They ain't going to hear about it," Simon grunted, "unless we put some distance between us and those braves. They're going to be mighty touchy about us stealing their horses." The three men rode on to the Ohio River. They hoped to cross it quickly and be well into Kentucky before the Indians reached the river, but a brisk fall wind drove choppy waves at them from the far bank. No matter how hard they tried, they couldn't coax the horses to enter the angry looking water.

"Maybe it'll let up by morning," Montgomery said. "We might as well stake out the horses and call it a day." George agreed.

"We'd better put another night's distance between us and the Shawnee," Simon warned.

"Hell!" Montgomery snorted. "Them Injuns are on foot. It'll take 'em two days to catch up with us." Simon shrugged and got off his horse. They staked out the animals and then doubled back on their trail to keep a lookout.

The next morning the river was still choppy, but they were determined to cross anyway. Simon slung his rifle over his shoulder and led the horses into the water. Once the animals lost their footing, however, they turned back to land.

"It's no damn good," Simon said. "We'll never get them to cross the river the way it's blowing up. We'd better pick out the three best of the bunch and ride down the river." This time the other two scouts agreed. They each chose a horse, set the others free, and started downstream at a hard gallop.

After riding for an hour, Montgomery suddenly pulled his horse up. "To hell with them damned redskins," he said. "I want the rest of my horses. I'm going back!"

"I'm with you!" George shouted and turned his horse.

"Don't be fools," Simon argued. "Chances are the Indians

have reached our camp. Let's keep the horses we have and be thankful we still have our scalps!"

"I'm going back!" Montgomery insisted.

"Me too!" George echoed. The two men turned their horses and rode off at a gallop. Simon hesitated, then he, too, turned back—and cursed himself for being a fool.

Rounding up the wild horses wasn't easy, but they had six of the ponies hobbled when Simon suddenly reined in sharply. Ahead of him, three braves and an English sergeant were riding down the trail. Simon quickly sprang off his horse and slipped through the brush. He pulled back the heavy hammer of his rifle, lifted it up to his shoulder, and waited. As the Indians rode across his line of vision, his sights fell dead on one brave's heart, and he squeezed the trigger. The hammer, with its large flint, snapped forward, throwing off sparks that glowed brightly. There was a sharp flash and Simon waited for the recoil of the weapon. It never came. His trusted rifle had flashed in the pan; the charge was still wet from his swim earlier that morning. Before Simon had a chance to reload, the Indians, hearing the snap of the hammer, closed in around him.

Grabbing his rifle by the barrel, he swung it back across his shoulder, prepared to brain the first man who came at him. But before he could bring it around he was dragged to the ground from behind.

As Simon fell, Montgomery raced up and fired his rifle at the braves. He missed and ducked back into the woods. A dozen warriors who had suddenly appeared out of nowhere followed him. There was another shot followed by a volley.

Simon was dragged to his feet when the party returned. They were all smiling, but the one who smiled the broadest was carrying a freshly-cut scalp. It was Montgomery's.

"You Simon Butler!" one of the braves said angrily—he was Chief Blackfish's son. "You steal our horses, you scalp many of our warrior."

"Kill him!" the other braves shouted.

"No!" Blackfish's son grunted. "He is a great Long Knife.

He must not die quickly. We will turn him over to the chiefs for torture."

"Scalp him," the braves shouted again, looking at Simon's red hair.

However, Blackfish's son ordered, "we will camp here tonight and return to the village tomorrow." The braves threw Simon to the ground and put a long heavy branch across his chest. The weight of it almost crushed the air out of his lungs. Then they tied his wrists to the branch with rawhide. His legs were pulled apart and bound to stakes driven deep into the ground.

That night was hell. The rawhide cut off his circulation and his hands and feet went numb. The next morning, they set out on the trail toward Chillicothe. On the second night, the braves stopped to set up their camp only a short distance from the village. They had decided to march their prisoner into Chillicothe the next day, but word of their important capture leaked out and soon the entire population had rushed out to see the prisoner.

"Bring the Long Knife to us so that he may hear us judge him," Chief Blackfish said. Simon was led in and was allowed to sit unbound before the gathering of braves. "You have done much to harm my people," Blackfish said to him. "The council has decided that you shall burn at the stake tomorrow!" The braves at the council whooped. "But my brothers," Blackfish said, holding up his hand, "if this Long Knife dies tomorrow, we shall rob many of our people of the right to beat him. I say he should run the gantlet in all Shawnee villages, and that he should be tortured at the stake where all people from our tribes can see him. Let us vote!" Blackfish picked up the ceremonial tomahawk at his side and passed it to the brave next to him. By passing it, he signified that Simon should live to run the other gantlet. A brave drove the tomahawk into the ground; that stood for immediate death. And so the tomahawk was passed from hand to hand. One brave carefully kept count of the vote with marks on the ground. When it was over, he tallied the marks. Simon was saved by one vote.

Once the decision had been reached, Simon was given food so that he would be strong enough to make the long march through the woods and run the gantlets waiting for him. The first was at Pickaway, and Simon saw the gantlet before he saw the village itself. But now he was prepared. He knew the secret of beating the gantlet and burst through the lines and fled to the council house in record time. All but two of the blows aimed at him missed. Then the braves escorted him to the next village.

The braves led him along the trail to Wapotomika. They were tired of their sport and were anxious to burn him at the stake. Simon stood at the head of the gantlet until he felt the knife in his back urging him on. He sprang ahead, then cut sharply to his right, crashed through the lines of Indians, and made for the forest. A scream of frustration broke from the Indians, and they took after him on foot. But Simon had long legs and there wasn't a brave among them who could come close to running him down.

Simon ran for his life. Even when he had outdistanced the Indians, he continued to sprint through the woods. He wanted to stop and catch his breath, but each step took him closer to freedom and he forced himself on. Unexpectedly, he ran right into the middle of a war party returning from a bitter fight in Kentucky. They struck him down, bound his arms and legs, and dragged him back to the village.

As the days passed, Simon began to hope for rescue, and suddenly help came from a completely unexpected source. Peter Druillard was a fabulous French Canadian who had traded with the Indians for years. As a matter of fact, they treated him as one of their own. But on this trip he had important business with them. He was delivering the money that the British had promised the Indians for fighting the settlers. As paymaster, he could be as generous or tightfisted as he wanted, and Logan and Girty had asked that he use his influence to save Simon.

"I hate the Long Knives as much as you do," he told the council of chiefs. "They started this war which has taken the lives of many of your braves, but we will finish it by driving them back out of Kentucky. All we need is information. If the British officers could question the prisoner, they would learn much from him." Druillard paused and nodded at the chiefs. "If you turn him over to me to take to the British, I will pay you one hundred dollars." There was a mixed reaction from his audience. Druillard raised his hand. "Anyway, you can have him back after the English officers have finished questioning him." That did it. Simon was turned over to Peter Druillard and taken to Detroit.

Once the English officers discovered that Simon wasn't going to talk, they gave up questioning him and allowed him the run of the fort. All he had to do was report to an officer every morning and stay within one mile of the fort at all times. Being a prisoner of war was a luxury after his ordeal with the Indians. Simon's first thought was to escape, but winter was closing in and he had neither the clothing nor the arms to make a break through the wilderness. He settled down to enjoy the winter and to make as many friends as possible. That was easy for the goodnatured Simon, and he was soon talking to almost everyone at the fort.

Simon drew out all the traders who came to the fort. Finally, he had the information he needed for an escape but he still needed arms. He had made friends with the storekeeper and his wife at the fort. One day he spoke with the woman. "Seems a shame," he said, "that on warm spring days like this a man can't get out into the woods and shoot himself a little game."

She didn't answer right away. "The Indians will be bringing their furs to the fort in another week," she said hesitantly. "Sometimes they're mighty careless with their rifles." Simon smiled and said no more.

The Indians came with their furs, and after the trading was over they relaxed with a few jugs of whiskey. No one saw a stack of three rifles disappear. That night, Simon and two friends met behind the store. Neatly piled and waiting for them were powder, lead, and food. The storekeeper and his wife were loyal British subjects, but they weren't going to let men starve to death in the wilderness.

The first few days out of Detroit, they hid during the day and traveled at night. The going was rugged. The route Simon chose led through unbroken forests, and broad swamps; even the Indians avoided the area. There wasn't a hint of a trail for them to follow, but Simon unerringly led them toward the Ohio River. Twice, when they were on high ground, they almost stumbled onto Indian hunting parties, but both times they slipped away. Seven weeks after they had left Detroit, they reached Clark's settlement on the Ohio River.

Simon relaxed for a few weeks and regained his strength, but that was all the civilization he could take. Besides, he had work to do. The power of the Indians in Kentucky had to be broken once and for all, and he set out to join George Rogers Clark and his army.

"You're not as dead as I thought you'd be," Clark chuckled when he saw Simon. "You looking to be my scout?" Simon nodded, and the men sat down to a good drink. Simon gave Clark a complete description of the fort at Detroit and the number of men holding it.

"They're too strong for us," Clark said, shaking his head. "I was hoping to take the fort before winter, but I'll need more men!"

"How about hitting another target?" Simon asked.

"Do you have one for me?"

Simon grinned. "The Shawnee villages," he said. "If we destroyed them before winter, the Indians would have their hands full just keeping alive. They wouldn't have time to raid our villages."

Simon led the way and Clark's army followed him. One after the other, the villages where Simon had been forced to run the gantlet were burned to the ground. The first village was Chillicothe. This time Simon approached it proudly, as a conquerer instead of as a captive. But when they arrived, the village was already in ruins. The Indians had been warned of their approach. The army swept further west. Soon a dozen villages had been destroyed along with stores of food. They met little resistance, and when they were through, the strength of the Indians in Kentucky was broken for good.

Back at Clark's settlement, Simon spun in surprise when he heard his name called out. "Kenton—Simon Kenton!" A man strode up to him with his hand held out. It was the first time in a decade that Simon had heard his real name. He studied the man's face for a clue. "John Leachman," the man said. "How are you, lad?"

Suddenly the old fear flashed back. He answered Leachman's questions and then hesitated. Leachman sensed his feeling and suddenly grinned. "You thinking about Ellen and Will?" he asked. "The two of 'em were having one hell of a time raising all their kids the last time I saw them."

With that, the guilt was finally lifted from Simon's mind, and he returned to Virginia to visit his family. He had left in disgrace, but came back a hero. In a short time the whole family was packed onto wagons and headed back to Kentucky with him.

Simon Kenton continued to scout for years afterwards. Even after he married, he didn't settle down until the frontier had pushed past him and he was too old to follow it. He died quietly in his sleep in 1836, in Urbana, Illinois. Many years later they erected a monument over his grave.

Simon Kenton had found a wilderness in Kentucky. He had hunted in it, and then scouted for the farmers who followed him. Finally, he made it safe for them by driving out the Indians. Some people said he was a great man, but Ellen Cummins never did believe it. She always insisted that the prophecy she had made years before was the right one. Simon was good-natured, but he could never make a farmer.

Davy Crockett
King of the Wild Frontier

By JACK PEARL

Bear hunter, Indian fighter, champion of the people, this irrepressible backwoodsman carved a notch in American folklore with his famous rifle Betsy, his knife, his gifted tongue, and his last-ditch stand at the Alamo

Davy Crockett! It's a name that conjures up a picture of a fierce heroic figure with a bloody gash across his forehead, standing knee-deep in bodies in a corner of a crumbling stone fort, his splintered rifle thrown to one side, a gory Bowie knife in one hand, and the fingers of his other hand twisted in the hair of a dying Mexican soldier at his feet. Before him, cringing and yelping like a bunch of jackals held at bay by a wounded lion, stands half the Mexican Army. And, if you remember your grammar school history lessons, you may be able to call to mind the motto emblazoned across the top of that history book's page: "Liberty and Independence Forever!"

It's a stirring picture—if a bit melodramatic—and substantially an accurate representation of Crockett's fighting death. Undeniably Davy and the Alamo go together like MacArthur and Bataan. Yet one can't help but reflect upon the sad truth that men are better remembered for the way they die than for the way they live.

David Crockett was the fifth child of six boys and three girls born to John Crockett, a Tennessee Irishman who was far more successful at increasing his family than he was at increasing his fortune. John Crockett was a good father and he loved his children, but he was a resourceful man who didn't believe in idle assets. As soon as they were old enough, his daughters went into domestic service in the homes of the local gentry; his sons went to work long before they were old enough. At the age of eight, Davy was hired out to a Dutch merchant as a journeyman's boy. But being a lad who bridled against harsh authority, he slipped away one night while his master was sleeping, taking care first to extract his back wages from the Dutchman's pocketbook. Then he hiked home, seventy miles through the wild forest, as nonchalantly as a modern schoolboy walks home after class.

John Crockett was mildly displeased at the way the arrangement had turned out, but he was glad to see his son. After giving the matter considerable thought, he decided that as long as Davy wouldn't work, the next best thing was to send him to school. Unhappily, Davy didn't hit it off with the schoolmaster any better than he had with the Dutchman. Each year it was worse. The climax came one day when the teacher sent him to the big blackboard on the front wall of the schoolroom and told him to write down all the words he could spell. Davy took him literally. Now most schoolmasters of the pioneer era knew it was almost as dangerous to turn your back on a pupil as it was to turn it on a renegade Indian, but this fellow must have been new at the game. Complacently, he faced the class and began to read from a volume of Elizabethan poetry. It wasn't long before he woke up to the fact that there was an unusual amount of grinning and snickering going on. Imagining that young Crockett was making faces at him behind his back, and hoping to catch the culprit off guard, he whirled around. To his surprise, Davy was absorbed in the assignment. The tip of his tongue was clenched between his teeth as he blocked out the letters painfully on the blackboard. The schoolmaster started to turn back to the class; then his eyes bulged like a bullfrog's. With the exception of "boy" and 'girl," which headed the list of words, the rest of the column contained all the rude four-letter Anglo-Saxon words the schoolmaster had ever heard, plus some he hadn't heard. When he was able to speak, he let out a roar that silenced the tittering in the classroom, "Master Crockett!"

Davy turned an impassive face, "Yes, sir?"

A tic worked grotesquely in the teacher's sallow face. He pointed a long trembling finger at the heavy birch switch that stood in one corner of the room. "The birch, Master Crockett!"

Davy craned his neck inquisitively. "Nothin' wrong with it that I can see." A boy in the front row let out a loud guffaw.

"None of your impudence, Crockett!" The master's voice trembled hysterically. "Bring it here at once!"

Without a word, Davy walked over, picked up the stick, and hefted it experimentally in his hands.

"Bring it here!"

Davy came to within a few feet of the teacher and stopped. His black eyes were impish and bright.

The master held out his bony hand, palm up. "Give it to me."

Davy's eyes traveled around the sea of smirking faces, traveled to the teacher's hand, and finally rested on the switch. Then, with the fine sense of the theatrical that was to serve him so well in later life, he brought the birch whistling down on the teacher's outstretched palm. While the children hooted and yelled and the teacher hooted and hopped about, shaking his smarting member, Davy made a spectacular exit through the open window.

Later that day, one of his older brothers discovered Davy

propped against a shady tree on the bank of the river, strumming his battered mouth harp. "Teacher's gonna give you the devil in three or four different ways, Davy," he said seriously.

Davy gave him a broken-toothed grin as he wiped the harp on his buckskin shirt. "I don't think I'll be goin' to school for a spell, John."

"What about Paw? He's sure to hear about what happened."

"I thought about that too. I hear tell Jesse Creek's looking for hands to take his drove to Front Royal."

The older boy looked shocked. "Davy, you ain't gonna run away from home?"

Davy spit at a big frog squatting in the sun a few feet away. "Looks like the schoolmaster when he's workin' up a fit," he said absently. Then, in answer to the question, he asked, "You got a better idea?"

"It'll break Maw's heart if you run away."

Davy touched his bottom gingerly. "Right now I'm worryin' about my butt. When I think of that big hickory stick Paw carries . . ." He left his thought unfinished.

John Crockett moved his shoulders uncomfortably at the mention of the hickory. "Well I got to get back to my chores or I'll get it too."

"You do that, John. And tell Maw not to fret about me."

"All right, Davy." John turned away and walked slowly back along the path that led through the forest.

"Oh, John," Davy yelled after him, "give my best to the schoolmaster!"

Long after he was out of sight of the river, John Crockett could hear the flat, sing-song twang of the mouth harp drifting lazily over the treetops.

Davy Crockett got his first real taste of adventure driving Jesse Creek's oxen to Front Royal. Working and living with a bunch of rugged, ribald frontiersmen was a lot different than being a lackey for a crotchety Dutch journeyman. At night, around the campfire, Davy would listen with speechless, wide-eyed wonder to the tall and gusty talk of Indians, wild animals, and women that poured out of the men just as fast as the green whisky poured into them. It was good to sit on the bare earth, isolated from the darkness by the fire that blistered his face, with the chill of the night air on his neck and the silence of the forest at his back.

When the fire had died and the men were long silent, Davy would lie curled up in his blankets, too excited to sleep, staring hypnotically into the winking embers as he dreamed about the day when he would be able to do all the things the older men had done.

When the drove was sold in Front Royal and the hands had been paid off, Jesse Creek asked Davy if he was going back with them. Davy jingled the coins in his pocket, savoring the feeling of independence they gave him. "I don't reckon so, Jesse," he drawled. "So long as I've gone this far, I may as well see some of the world before I go home."

Jesse Creek laughed. "That's big talk from a boy your age."

Davy straightened up. "Everyone says I look a lot older than twelve."

"You do, at that," Jesse Creek had to admit as he appraised the boy's sturdy frame and noted with some surprise that Davy's black piercing eyes were almost on a level with his own.

"There's a lot of things I ain't never done," Davy went on. "And I don't expect to get 'em done sitting on my rump."

"Like what?" Jesse Creek smiled tolerantly.

"Like scalping redskins, hunting bear, and—and—" Davy looked down at the ground, a flush creeping up his neck. "And gettin' myself a woman."

"Gettin' yourself a woman!" Jesse Creek fought a losing battle to keep a straight face. "I declare, you *are* more man than I gave you credit for."

Davy shifted restlessly from one foot to the other. "A man needs room to grow in, Jesse, same as a tree."

Jesse Creek stared at him strangely. "You're an old one for your years, Davy. But don't forget, a tree needs roots, and so does a man. You remember that when you get tired of adventuring, Davy."

The boy pushed back a lick of jet black, shiny hair that hung across his forehead. "I'll remember, Jesse."

During the next two years Davy worked for a wagoner in Montgomery, Virginia, traveled with an itinerant blacksmith, and finally settled down in a steady job with a hatter in New River. Although he had yet to scalp an Indian, kill a bear, or know a woman, he had seen and learned a little more about life.

After one long and particularly wearisome day of tanning beaver skins for hats, Davy was eating a meager supper of bread and cheese in his sleeping quarters behind the shop, when the odor of hot, spiced apple pie wafted in through the window on the crisp fall air. His mouth began to water, and a vision of the aromatic pies and pastries his own mother used to bake came vividly to his mind. The Crocketts may have been poor, but they had always eaten well and amply. A lump formed in his throat, and he experienced a sharp longing to see his home and family again. He started for Tennessee early the next morning.

He was only about a day's traveling time away from his father's inn when he came face to face with his brother Tom in a Sullivan County tavern. To his amazement, Tom didn't recognize him; in fact, it took some convincing to wipe the incredulous expression off his face. "I never would of knowed you, Davy," Tom Crockett said in a mystified voice. "You're taller and wider. You even look different." He reached over and fingered the long mane of black hair that hung almost shoulder length around Davy's dark, strong-featured face, and studied that face wonderingly.

Davy's lips curved in a mischievous grin. "Say, Tom, you reckon Maw and Paw might not know me either?"

"I'll bite a skunk's tail out if they do."

Davy began to laugh. "Let's have some fun with 'em."

The next day Tom Crockett arrived home with a tall stranger in a coonskin cap, whom he introduced as Mr. Peabody. "Mr. Peabody's come to bring us news of Davy," he said, casting his eyes down gravely. John Crockett began to mutter in his thick Irish brogue. Mrs. Crockett put a hand to her heart, and the children babbled excitedly. The whole family gathered around the stranger. "Mr. Peabody" removed his coonskin cap and wiped it across moist eyes. "It pains me to be the one to bring you these sad tidings," he said in a voice thick with emotion.

Mr. Crockett moaned, "Somethin's happened to Davy!"

The stranger nodded. "He was comin' home. Would have made it too, only he couldn't get anyone to ferry him across the New River. It was all swollen from the freshet. That didn't stop Davy though. He tried to swim it."

"He drownded!" Mrs. Crockett sobbed.

The stranger shook his head. "Not a bit of it. He wasn't even puffin' when he reached the other side."

John Crockett's eyes widened in awe. "Davy always did take to the water."

"But just as he was dragging himself ashore, this prodigious rattlesnake came out of the woods and bit him on the left foot. Just about then this big alligator came swimming along, lean and hungry looking. Quick as a wink, Davy gave him the alligator mating call. The old feller squinted his way, but he wasn't too sound of sight, so he came swimmin' over to where Davy was. Not battin' an eye, Davy stuck his foot right into that 'gator's jaws, figurin' smartly that the beast would chaw it off, poison and all. He figured right too."

Beads of perspiration stood out on John Crockett's forehead. "Gor!" he exclaimed. "Never let it be said that the Crocketts are lackin' in gumption."

The children clustered around their wailing mother and tried to comfort her. The stranger put his coonskin cap back on his head and blew his nose on a red bandanna. "It was a terrible thing to see. But it still would've come out all right, except for one thing. He'd put the wrong foot into the 'gator's mouth . . . Just before he closed his eyes, he says to me, 'Peabody, tell my old Paw he was right!' "

"And what did he mean by that?" John Crockett looked puzzled.

"He says to me, 'Peabody, Paw always told me I didn't

know my left foot from my right, and that's been my down-fall.' "

There was an uneasy silence in the room; even Mrs. Crockett stopped crying. Suddenly there was a snicker from one of the girls. "Your name ain't Peabody!" she accused him.

"Do tell," answered the stranger, devilment written all over his face. Suddenly all eyes in the room were studying him closely. The girl giggled. "It's Davy Crockett!" she cried triumphantly.

The Crockett table was a groaning board that night. John Crockett even broke out a bottle of his best corn whisky. When they had finished off two of Mrs. Crockett's big apple pies, the family gathered around the fireplace, with Davy the center of attention as he reeled off yarns about his experiences of the past three years. There wasn't really so much to tell, but Davy added a little here and there, and spiced it up with his wit, and the family hung on every word. Striding up and down on the wide hearth like an actor on a stage, with a cup of whisky in one hand and the corncob pipe which his father had filled for him in the other, Davy was filled with a sense of exhilaration and contentment. Such unaccustomed privileges meant only one thing to him. He was a man at last.

But Davy was soon to find out that manhood had its drawbacks as well as its advantages. The following week, he went to work for a rich Quaker in order to help pay off a thirty-six dollar note on his father's inn. It took a full year to settle the debt. Then, because his own buckskin clothing and moccasins were threadbare and beyond mending, he agreed to put in another year's service to pay for some store-bought clothing and shoes. The Quaker's twenty-one-year-old-niece, Anna, pretty and blonde with a slim waist and soft curves, played some part in his decision.

One Saturday night, Davy got all decked out in his new clothes and perched his old coonskin hat on his head. He threw an old blanket across his mule, mounted her, and set out to pay a visit to the Quaker's niece. His gangling legs hung down the sides of the mule, and as he bobbed up and down, his new shoes kept scuffing up the dust. As he rode, he raised his eyes to the big orange moon balanced on the edge of the forest and began to bellow:

> *A cow needs a bull, and a bull needs a cow,*
> *A sow needs a pig, and a pig needs a sow,*
> *No critter can fight it, it's sad to relate,*
> *Yes woman needs man and man needs his mate.*

Some thirty-odd verses later, Davy pulled up at the Quaker's place. And as soon as he and the girl were comfortably seated on a log bench on the porch, he blurted out his proposal. "My love is so hot as might nigh to burst my boilers, Anna," he told her. "Will you marry me?"

"I'm mighty flattered, Davy," Anna said kindly. "But you know I'm already spoken for."

"You can explain to him, can't you?"

"But I *want* to marry him."

Davy scratched his head thoughtfully. "And you don't want to marry me?"

"I like you a heap, Davy," she smiled. "But I don't want to marry you."

"It's on account of I ain't got no education, is that it?"

The girl put her small hand on top of his. "That's not it at all. You're a fine man, Davy. I'd be proud to marry you if—"

"If what?"

"If I loved you."

Davy gazed solemnly at her hand, so tiny and white against his big brown paw. A broad grin spread across his face in the darkness. "Appears I have a great deal better opinion of myself than others have."

Davy couldn't get to sleep that night. Finally he rolled out of bed, pulled on his pants, and went out into the yard back of the house. With his back braced against a log, he lit up a pipe and began to pick out chords on a battered guitar the Quaker had given him. He sang slowly, sadly. The songs he sang were sweet and weighted with trouble, as only folk music strummed on a guitar on a lonely summer night can be

A little later Davy's older brother came out of the house, running his hands through tousled hair.

"What you makin' all that ruckus for, Davy?"

Davy looked up, his fingers still moving over the strings of the guitar. "Can't sleep, Tom. Sorry if I woke you up."

Tom Crockett scratched himself vigorously. "You beat everything, Davy. You been mooning around like a sick calf."

"Tom," Davy said earnestly, "they say there's a lid for every pot, but I ain't so certain any more."

"What you talkin' about?"

"The gals I like never seem to like me, and them that likes me are as homely as stone fences."

Tom Crockett squatted down on his haunches and laughed. "I declare, I believe a visit to the Dutch widow's daughter is what you need."

Davy shuddered. "I'd sooner let old Doc Brown pull out my teeth. She's so ugly it hurts me to look at her. I wish I may be shot if it doesn't."

Tom winked. "She does a feller a lot more good than Doc Brown can."

"That must be so," Davy conceded, seeing's she does far more trade than the Doc does."

"Why don't you ask her to the dance Friday night?"

"I can't dance."

"Who said anything about dancing?"

"Well," Davy said lamely, "maybe I will. Sometimes, when a feller's lost, the way home is just the way he don't think it is."

The words were prophetic. For although Davy took the widow's daughter to the dance, he went home with a pretty brown-haired girl named Polly. Inside of a few months they were married. They rented a farm and a cabin with fifteen dollars, which the Quaker gave them for a wedding present, and Davy settled down to raise crops. Polly attended to her spinning and weaving and all the many tasks that a good farmer's wife was expected to manage. She bore Davy two sons. It was a good life, but unrewarding for an ambitious man with the spirit of adventure in him.

One night, when they were lying close in bed in the darkness, Davy said to Polly, "Before I got a wife I thought I needed nothing else in the world. Now, having a wife, I want everything else in the world. You deserve better than I can ever give you."

Polly took his hand and pressed it to her face, "I never wanted more than you to begin with."

He began to stroke her cheek gently with his rough, calloused fingers, marveling, as he always did, that anything in the world could be that soft. "It's getting so I can't breathe here, Polly. I'm getting like those scrub pines that grow on the hill back of the shack, all shriveled up and dry. I want to grow like one of those big oak trees, poking its head up into the sky where it can look out over the world. Don't you ever feel you'd like to get out of here, Polly?"

"Anything you say, Davy," was the quiet answer.

He realized with a start that his fingers moving on her face were wet. "Polly! What's the matter? You're crying."

"I'm not."

"You don't want to leave here; that's it," he said hastily. "All right, we won't. It really ain't bad. We got enough to eat and a roof over our heads. I got two fine boys and you. Heck, what more could a man want?"

"You're sweet, Davy," Polly whispered. "Honest, though, I ain't got my heart set on staying here. Long as I got you, I can be happy anywhere."

"You *are* the best wife going, Polly Crockett." He pulled her against him roughly and kissed her.

Polly giggled softly in the darkness. "Shhh—you'll wake up the boys."

That spring Davy moved his family across the mountains into Lincoln County. He built a cabin at the head of the Mulberg fork of the Elk River and settled down to become a hunter and trapper. He stayed there seven years before the old restlessness got him. Then he pulled up stakes again and made a new home on Bean Creek in Franklin County.

About that time there were persistent rumors in the backwoods country that war with England was imminent, but no one paid much attention to them. News had a way of getting distorted and magnified by the time it got to the frontier, and the settlers had learned to discount sensational stories. They were shocked out of their apathy when the Creek Indians, supported and egged on by the British, opened a full-scale war against the United States with the infamous massacre at Fort Mims. Fort Mims was a flourishing little community on the border of Indian territory. Years of peace had lulled the settlers and their families into a sense of false security. The settlement had outgrown the undermanned garrison. There was only a handful of soldiers stationed there, and the discipline was lax. One morning, without warning, an army of Creeks swept down on the fort, burning and pillaging, slaughtering and torturing men, women, and children impartially. There was only one survivor. He escaped by running across the heads of a panic-stricken mob herded together on one side of the stockade, leaping to the top of the wall, and jumping to safety. His moving account of the tragedy spread through the forest like a crown fire and created an uproar all along the frontier. The immediate reaction of stunned surprise was followed by hot indignation and outraged demands for reprisal. But there wasn't any real action, for it had been so many years since the country had been in a war that no one knew anything about it.

Finally Davy Crockett proposed that they all stop talking and ride over to Winchester, where a muster was being taken, and join up. That put the damper on emotions. Most of the men began to stutter excuses and drift away to their cabins.

When Davy told Polly that he was going to enlist to fight the Creeks, she started to cry. Davy took her in his arms and tried to console her as best he could, but his mind was made up. "If every man waited until his wife got ready for him to go off to war," he said, "there wouldn't be much fightin' done."

The next morning he and his best friend, George Russell, saddled up their ponies and headed for Winchester to join the volunteers. Major Gibson, the commander, was glad to see them; he needed expert woodsmen and scouts. Besides, Davy had already gained a modest reputation as a marksman, shooting for sides of beef at local rifle matches.

A few days later, the column began the long march to the Tennessee River, recruiting more troops at every town they passed through. By the time they reached their destination they had about thirteen thousand mounted volunteers. The orders were to sit tight and wait for General Andrew Jackson and the main army moving up from Nashville, but Major Gibson decided to send patrols across the river to scout up information about the movements of the Creeks. Davy Crockett was the first man to volunteer; the major put him in charge of a party of thirteen scouts.

For two days Davy and his men rode cautiously into Indian territory without seeing a sign of a hostile. Then they met a friendly half-breed who told them that a Creek army numbering thousands was only a day's march away, moving up to invade Kentucky. The scouts galloped back to the river to spread the alarm.

Major Gibson immediately ordered breastworks thrown up for a quarter of a mile along the banks of the Tennessee, and he sent a messenger back to Fayetteville, where Jackson's army was encamped, to tell the general the Creeks were coming. "It don't look good, Crockett," the major said, smacking his lips after taking a long pull from a flask Davy had offered him. "If the Creeks get to us before Old Hickory does—" He didn't bother to finish.

Davy took a long rope of tobacco out of a pocket in his loose buckskin jacket and bit off a hunk. "You know, Major, there's only two things a little man can do when he's facing up to a big man who's itching for a scrap. He can turn tail and run, or he can step up while the big feller's taking off his coat and clout him square in the chops."

The major's eyebrows went up high. "What have you got in mind, Crockett?"

"Just this. Them redskins will be expecting us to wait on them this side of the river. What would they be apt to think if we was to come chargin' down on them like the Mexican Cavalry before they ever got to the river?"

There was a calculating gleam in the major's eyes. "Why, they'd probably suspect Old Hickory's army had growed wings and got here two days ahead of time."

Davy winked wisely. "If they don't, my name's not Davy Crockett. Anyway, it ought to give 'em some aggravation for thought. By the time they get over thinking about it, maybe General Jackson *will* be here!"

Major Gibson was smiling now. "How many men do you think you'd need to pull it off?"

"Oh, eight hundred or thereabouts." Davy suddenly did a double take. "Did you say how many men would *I* need?"

Major Gibson was smiling broadly. "That's right, *Sergeant* Crockett!"

Davy grinned sheepishly, showing his big yellow teeth. "Well, that's mighty nice of you, Major."

That afternoon Davy led his small army across the river and struck inland for a location he had marked out on a rough map sketched during his scouting expedition. It was a spot where the trail passed through a valley between a small range of wooded hills. Davy spread out his men in a thin line on the ridges of the hills, flanking the trail on both sides, and sat down to wait for the Creeks. He didn't have to wait long. As a thin edge of silver showed on the eastern horizon, the advance scouts of the Creek Army came padding silently out of the blackness of the west and started up the ridge. Like stalking cats, dark shapes rose up from bushes behind the Indians or dropped onto their backs from overhanging tree limbs. Knives, their blades coated with stoveblack to hide even the faintest reflection of light, struck swiftly and efficiently in the darkness. There were moans and faint scuffling noises, but these were lost in the rustling and twittering of the birds in the treetops, preening themselves for the new day.

In the blue haze of dawn, the first detachment of the Creek Army, about three thousand strong, began to move through the valley. Looking down on the Indians from the top of the ridge, Davy turned to George Russell. "Soon's I give the sign, we'll go charging down, hollerin,' and shootin' all at once. They'll think the whole U. S. Cavalry is after 'em. If we can stampede these Injuns in the valley back into the main column, the chances are the whole mob will turn tail. Fear's like fever. It's catchin'.'"

As the first Indians reached the head of the pass, a single shot rang out, echoing back and forth across the valley. All at once the peaceful looking hills came alive with smoke and fire as the long lines of mounted militiamen swept down the slopes on the Creeks' flanks. Taken by surprise, the Indians milled about in mad disorder. There was no chance for organized resistance. Horses reared and plunged in all directions, tripping over one another in their panic. The Creek riders, skillful as they were, had all they could do to keep from being thrown. They had no chance to return the fire. The instinct for survival dominated all else. There was a wild melee at the approaches of the valley as a wave of retreating Indians ran into the main body of advancing Creeks. The leaders tried to rally their forces, but as more and more men came flying back, shrieking that the whole American Army was on their heels, the ranks wavered and finally broke. Soon the whole Creek Army was spreading out across the plains to the west in full retreat, leaving their dead and wounded behind.

The next day General Jackson's army arrived at the camp after a forced march from Fayetteville. Jackson's men were thoroughly exhausted, in no condition to fight Indians. But Davy's little stratagem had accomplished its purpose. It stalled the Creeks in their tracks for two days, just enough time for Jackson's men to get their wind and for the general to map out a battle plan. When the fight finally was joined, the Indians suffered four hundred casualties and a shocking blow to their confidence.

With that victory under their belts, Jackson's troopers rolled on to even bigger victories at Fort Williams, and then Tallapoosa River, where one of the most vital and bloodiest battles of the campaign was waged. Jackson was crossing the

Tallapoosa near Horseshoe Bend, when the Creeks swooped down unexpectedly from the front and rear. The soldiers fell back on both sides of the river until half the army was fighting waist-deep in water. Everywhere there was chaos; officers deserted, horses reared and threw their riders, the river ran red blood.

Digging his spurs into his pony, Davy Crockett plunged through a tangle of floating corpses and rode up to Governor Carroll of Tennessee. 'We've been damned fools trying to fight these bastards on both sides of the river at the same time," he argued. "They only got a small force at our rear. If we pull out of the west bank, I think we can save our skins."

"Damned if I don't think you're right, Crockett!" Carroll roared. "Let's try and rally the men!"

Virtually usurping command from Andrew Jackson, Governor Carroll rallied what was left of the army around him and regained the east bank from the Creeks. Drunk with success and overeager to put the *coup de grace* to the enemy, the Indians swarmed into the river with wild war whoops, certain that they had the white men on the run. But Jackson's men did a quick about-face and deployed along the river bank. They let the Creeks get almost to the shore, then laid down a withering barrage of rifle fire on them. The bewildered, angry Indians found themselves in the same predicament the white men had been in only minutes before. The Creek chieftains refused to believe that the white men could continue their resistance for long after the staggering losses they had suffered, so they kept driving their warriors across the river in repeated and unsuccessful attacks. And as a gambler, obsessed with the idea that he can't lose if he keeps trying, fritters away his fortune on the wheel, so the Creeks squandered their army in the bloody river.

With the organized Creek uprising on the frontier at an end—there would be minor resistance for years to come— General Jackson took his army south to meet the British threat in Florida. Davy Crockett went home after his enlistment was up, but he didn't have much heart for hunting and trapping. His appetite fell off, he couldn't sleep, his children

got on his nerves, and he was indifferent to Polly. One day
she said to him, "Davy, what's come over you? You're plumb
cantankerous since you come home from the war. You're
about as easy to get close to as a porcupine."

"I'm sorry, Polly," he apologized. "It's just that there's
still fightin' to be done, and I don't feel right about quittin'
on Old Hickory like I did. A man ain't got no right to walk
out on a war like he does on a church meeting."

"You done your share."

"That ain't no way to look at it. No one's done his share
if he walks off a job 'fore it's finished."

Polly came to the back of his chair and put her arms
around his neck. "I sort of see what you mean, Davy," she
said quietly. "If you want to go with Andy Jackson, Davy, I
won't try and stop you."

Major Russell and his volunteers were on their way to join
Jackson at Pensacola, when Davy caught up with them. "It's
a comfort to have you and Betsy with us again, Crockett,"
the major said, patting Davy's long rifle fondly.

Davy grinned. "It's good to be here. Those redcoats ought
to make mighty fine targets."

But Davy was in for a disappointment. When they got to
Pensacola, Jackson had already taken the town and was preparing to march to the defense of Mobile. The militia was
given the job of mopping up the little bands of hostile Creeks
that were still scattered throughout the territory. "I was set
on gettin' a whack at those British," Davy grumbled. "But
I suppose I might as well finish up the job I started."

Major Russell's army marched to Fort Mims, the ill-fated
settlement where the Creek War had first been ignited, and
set up a field headquarters. Nature had all but reclaimed the
once lively little community. The ashes of the burned buildings were hidden in thick underbrush. The few structures
that were still standing were sagging badly and eaten away by
mildew, as was the crumbling palisade. But the soldiers soon
found out about one cheerful aspect of life at their new
station. At the time of the massacre, herds of cattle and pigs
had been grazing all around Fort Mims. Now these animals

were running wild in the forest and were fair game for the starving soldiers. To add to the windfall, a barge arrived the same afternoon loaded with coffee, sugar, and rum. That night Fort Mims was resurrected in a whirl of song and laughter, feasting and drinking. Men huddled around hundreds of campfires, bleary-eyed from rum, their stomachs stuffed with strips carved from huge quarters of beef turning slowly on blackened spits. Tom-toms beat out a weird rhythm as friendly Chickasaw and Choctaw Indians staged a primitive war dance around their fires, naked except for their crimson plumes, moccasins, and fringed leggings.

There was too much excitement for Davy to sit still. All night long he moved from fire to fire about the camp, swigging from a bottle at one party, cramming a piece of smoking meat in his mouth at another. He could never remember a time when he had felt more alive. Life at home was spiritless compared to this. The banks of the Alabama were ringing with the music and comaraderie of war. He felt guilty as he thought of Polly, patiently waiting at home.

When his enlistment was up this time, he knew he was ready to go home. He rode continuously for two days and nights, so great was his desire to get there. Just before dawn on the third day, he sighted his cabin sitting dark and peaceful in a grove of fir trees at the side of the trail. Davy grinned to himself in the dark. "Must all be asleep. I think I'll go chargin' in, growling like a bear, and rouse 'em out proper." He tethered his horse at the back of the cabin and tiptoed around to the front door. He stumbled in the darkness and fell to his knees. He cursed softly and felt around with his hands to find out what had tripped him. It was a mound of earth about two feet wide and six feet long. Davy gasped, fear burning in his throat like acid. "Feels like a grave," he whispered hoarsely, licking at a rivulet of sweat that had run down his face into the corner of his mouth. He sat there numbly for a long time, too weak to move. Then, in the first faint glimmer of daylight filtering through the trees to the east, he made out a white wooden cross at the upper end of the mound. There was a name on the crosspiece printed in black letters: Polly Crockett.

For weeks Davy Crockett sat alone in his cabin grieving over his wife's death. When Polly had first come down with fever, her sister had taken the Crockett children to her home. Davy decided to let them stay there until he could make other arrangements. Friends dropped in and tried to cheer him up, but he kept staring into the fire or out of the window, nodding politely, hardly listening to what they were saying. Even his beloved "Betsy" stood neglected in the corner, gathering dust and showing the first traces of rust along the barrel.

One day George Russell stopped by with a full jug. He took two mugs from the shelf, blew the dust off them, and filled them up. He handed one to Davy. "Drink up, boy. You're going to need it. I got some news to tell you."

Davy drained the cup indifferently. "What kind of news?"

George sat down on a chair and began to sip his whisky appreciatively. "Since the war, Davy, a lot of newcomers have settled here. We're becoming an important town in these parts. For some time now, there's been a cry for law and order. Last night we held a meeting and elected a magistrate and a couple of constables. I got picked for one of the constables."

"That's mighty fine, George," Davy said, trying to show polite interest. "Who'd they make magistrate?"

Russell grinned into his cup, "Feller by the name of Davy Crockett."

Davy sat up straight in his chair.

"I'm mighty grateful, George, but I can't accept."

"Why not, Davy?"

Davy bridled irritably, " 'Cause I don't want to, that's why. Let 'em pick somebody else."

George Russell swished his whisky around the sides of the cup. "People used to ask your Polly why it was you didn't stay home like the other men after your first enlistment. You know what she told 'em? She said as long as there was work to be done, you weren't the kind to sit back and let the other feller do it. She was real proud of that, Davy."

"It ain't the same thing."

"Yes it is. There's work to be done here, Davy, lots of work. In less than a month, there's been two shootings and a mess of robberies, and two nights back a couple of farm-hands broke in Old Man Kelly's cabin and raped his sixteen-year-old daughter. That's only part of what's been goin' on since the town's built up." Russell finished his whisky and got up. Then he started for the door. "I'll tell 'em we better elect somebody else."

"Hold on, George!" Davy flung the contents of his cup into the fireplace and watched the flames lick up brightly on the logs. "You win. I'll do it."

Davy Crockett was a big success as a magistrate. Whenever a complaint was made against a man, he would issue a "verbal" warrant and his constables would bring the offender in. As magistrate Davy was a fair man, but not a particularly lenient one. He possessed common sense, a cool head, understanding of his fellow woodsmen, and the shrewdness of King Solomon. And he was always ready to back up his decisions with his fists or his famous rifle, which always was within easy reach when he held court.

Some months later, when the legislature incorporated Shoal Creeks with the other white settlements in the county, Davy was appointed a squire with the honorary title of colonel. "Looks like I'm going to have to learn how to read and write if I want to stay in politics," he told George Russell, waving around his new office at the shelves lined with law books.

George grinned. "You think you'll be staying in politics, Davy?"

"Maybe so. I don't like to walk off a job before it's finished, and God knows there's so much to be done in this country, a man couldn't scratch the surface in ten lifetimes. Then, from what I've seen, there's too many politicians who spend so much time butterin' their own bread that they don't have time to see that their constituents have any bread and butter on their tables."

"You figure you could make out against them slick-talking politicians with all their money and education and fancy manners?"

Davy winked broadly. "You remember one thing, George. Money and education and fancy manners ain't gonna do 'em any good if they don't get the votes, and them that does the votin' ain't taken with any of those things. They're *my* kind of people."

Russell squinted at him through a cloud of pipe smoke. "Danged if I don't believe you're getting ambitious, Davy Crockett."

Less than a year after Polly died, Davy married again. It was more of a marriage of convenience than anything else, for he had three small children to raise. Besides, he was a very lonely man. The second Mrs. Crockett was a well-to-do widow with substantial business interests and three small children of her own. She was a tall, comely woman, a few years older than Davy, with a strong character and a fair education. Davy had a great deal of respect and admiration for her. She, in turn, was quick to recognize the many unusual qualities in the big, uncouth backwoodsman, and she devoted much of her free time to tutoring him. He was an industrious student, and he made amazing headway, especially in reading and writing. In addition, he demonstrated his talent for leadership and organization by taking over the management of his wife's mills and distillery. For a time Davy was kept occupied with his official duties, business affairs, and his reading. But, gradually, the old restlessness came over him again.

In 1821, to the dismay of his close friends, he launched his campaign for the State Legislature. In this era it was generally accepted that politics was a rich man's hobby. The average backwoodsman had little understanding or interest in governmental matters. As long as his basic wants were satisfied, he didn't particularly care who represented him in the Legislature. The candidate who stood the best chance of winning an election was usually the one who made the most flowery speeches and could afford to give away the most whisky at the local voting rallies. It was the custom for a candidate to make the rounds of all the small towns and settlements in the county and talk personally with the people. He would pass out chaws of tobacco to all the men and urge them to attend the rallies to hear his speeches. Davy had one particular shirt with oversized pockets that he would stuff with tobacco and flasks of whisky. If possible, he preferred to follow the same route as one of the other candidates, greeting the settlers right after his opponent had moved on. He had a phenomenal memory and he made it his business to know the name and face of every voter in the community. A typical encounter ran something like this: "Well, hello, Sam Hawkins. How've you been? And how's the wife and the little ones?" At the same time he would pull out a flask of whisky and pass it down to the man who was just beginning to enjoy the chaw of tobacco which the other candidate had given him. Sam was now faced with an unpleasant choice. Either he had to spit out the tobacco or pass up the whisky. In almost every case, it was the tobacco that went. After he had had his drink and talked a while with Davy, poor Sam would usually cast a wistful glance at the tasty wad of tobacco that had gone to waste in the dirt. At this point, Davy would reach into his other pocket and pull out one of his long ropes of chewing tobacco.

"Here you are, Sam," Davy would smile. "Take a chaw of mine." Then with a sly wink, "There's one thing you can count on if you cast a vote for Crockett. I aim to leave every man on as good a footing as when I found him." It was amazing how many voters were impressed by this simple stratagem.

One day, at a big squirrel hunt and barbecue, Davy was challenged by another candidate to speak against him on the tariff. The truth was that this fellow never had taken Colonel Crockett very seriously. He knew the tall, ignorant backwoodsman had a reputation for being a wag, but he never thought of him as serious competition. Davy hemmed and hawed for a while, but at last the clamor for him was so great that he climbed up on the old tree stump set aside for the speechmaking and began:

"I reckon you folks know what I came for . . . your votes . . . And if you don't watch closely, I'll get 'em too." There was a round of applause, with even the rival candidate joining in. "Now about that tariff . . ." Davy stammered helplessly, for he knew nothing whatsoever about the tariff. When he tried to continue, it felt like his jaws were all stuck up with taffy. The other candidate was smiling and looking pleased with himself. In a halting voice, Davy went on to tell a few anecdotes about politicians and a joke or two, and in a few minutes he had the audience won over completely. Finally he finished up with ". . . And now, good people, I think I've been bending your ears long enough. I'm as dry as a powder horn, and I wouldn't be surprised if you could stand to wet your whistles too. If you'll do me the honor to join me, the drinks are on me." He hopped off the stump and set out for the liquor stands that had been erected at one side of the barbecue site, with most of the crowd at his heels. The other candidate quickly leaped on the stump and tried to rally the voters around him, but he couldn't even hear his own words over the stomping and cheering for Colonel Crockett.

The entire pattern of the election ran the same way. While the other candidates talked, Davy joked and laughed his way into the hearts of the people. He was elected to the legislature by a margin of nine votes, to represent the counties of Lawrence and Heckmann.

It is often said that the best way to teach a person how to swim is to throw him in the water when it's over his head. In the case of Davy Crockett, at least, it was true. The world of politics was as alien a climate to him as if he had been dropped on the moon. He was totally uninformed and uncultured. He had only the vaguest understanding of the matters which were introduced on the floor of the legislature. The vocabulary of his colleagues rendered a good part of the discussions completely unintelligible to him. But he was a good listener, and he had a memory like a sponge. He never forgot anything anyone said, and if he didn't understand a thing, he would wrestle with it until he could reduce it into terms that he did comprehend. He always formed definite opinions, and he wasn't embarrassed or afraid to stand up and voice them. He was extremely conscious of his great intellectual imperfections, although he was never diffident, and he read everything he could lay his hands on that he thought would make him better informed and better equipped to do his job.

In 1823 Colonel Crockett was re-elected to the legislature by a sizeable majority.

A Republican newspaper printed a scathing editorial lamenting the fact that the country had sunk so low that an ignorant bumpkin like Colonel Crockett could hold public office. Jokingly, the writer suggested that the backwoodsman would soon entertain ambitions to sit in the United States Congress. Davy read the article with amusement and commented mildly, "It just shows you, even a Republican can come up with a good idea once in a while. I never would have thought of running for Congress until now." When the 1824 elections for the House of Representatives got under way, Crockett's coonskin was the first hat tossed into the arena. But this time Davy was playing against major-league competition. His opposition to the popular tariff laws—the big issue of the campaign—was enough to defeat him in itself.

"You're a jackass, Davy," George Russell warned him. "When you talk against the tariff like you do, the farmers won't even drink your whisky, much less vote for you."

Davy put his hand on his friend's shoulder. "I always say a feller should make sure he's right and then go ahead, hell or high water. I'm sorry, George. I gave this a lot of careful thought, and I'm convinced this tariff will knock the price of cotton down to nothing."

Both men were right. Davy lost the election, and cotton dropped from twenty-five to six on the market. Although this was some salve for the defeat, Davy's pride was temporarily deflated. That autumn he decided to go into the barrel-stave business. In partnership with his friend Russell, he built two big river barges and loaded them with thirty thousand staves. They planned to sail down the Obion, into the Mississippi, and go all the way to New Orleans. When they were ready to leave, Russell, Davy, and Davy's youngest son went into the mountains to shoot some fresh meat to provision the two boats. They had only been out for a few hours when the dogs picked up a scent that sent their tails up stiff as ramrods. A minute later they were streaking through the early November snow with the two men and the boy running after them. The dogs were soon out of sight, their yelps growing fainter and fainter. Davy was afraid of losing track of them altogether, and he put on a burst of speed that left Russell and his son far behind. About ten minutes later he came upon the dogs clustered around the foot of a tree in a small open spot. Up in the tree was the biggest black bear Davy had ever seen. The bear was crouching halfway out on a limb, about ten feet above the ground, regarding his tormentors morosely and growling angrily deep down in his throat.

As he edged forward into the open, it was impossible for Davy to tell that the branch on which the bear was sitting was dead wood, for all the limbs were bare and dried up this late in the fall. Seeing that his quarry was safely treed, Davy decided to wait until his son and Russell arrived before he made the kill. He leaned his rifle against a tree and sauntered into the clearing, until he was directly beneath the bear.

"You're the biggest and meanest critter I ever did see!" he yelled. He stooped and picked up a handful of snow, and shaping it into an icy ball, pelted the bear with it. The dogs stopped worrying the tree trunk and gathered curiously around their master now, whining and wagging their tails. Davy had just bent over to get some more snow when there was a loud crack overhead. He looked up just in time to see the limb on which the bear was sitting break away cleanly from the trunk of the tree. Pushing hard with his heels he threw himself backward, but the soft snow slipped out from under him and he skidded flat on his back. The bear landed on all four feet, straddling Davy, and a second later the dogs were swarming over them from all sides.

When George Russell and Davy's son arrived on the scene, they were treated to a sight that drained the blood from their faces. Man, dogs, and bear were spinning around the clearing in a squirming ball of fur, fangs, buckskin, and snow, from which issued the most savage conglomeration of sounds that ever fell on a human ear—a ferocious medley of snarls, roars, and human blasphemy that made George Russell, who was not a particularly religious man, cross himself involuntarily.

Davy's son began to hop up and down shouting, "A b'ar's got my Paw! Shoot him, Mr. Russell! Shoot him!"

"Can't," Russell said weakly. "I might hit your Paw instead." He ducked as a shower of dirt flew into his face.

When the bear landed on top of him, Davy locked his legs over the animal's back and dug his hands into the shaggy fur on each side. Hugging himself close to the bear's belly and chest, he hung on grimly, just inside the sweeping claws and snapping fangs. For the time being at least, all the bear's attention was occupied in fighting off the hounds. Actually, Davy and the bear were receiving about equal punishment from this source, for in the fury of the battle, the dogs weren't too discriminating about whom or what they sank their teeth into. Meanwhile, Davy let go with his right hand and worked it slowly between his body and the bear's, toward the butcher knife in the sheath across his chest. It was a slow and precarious maneuver, for knocking around as they were, any sudden jolt might cause him to stab himself. But finally he got the knife clear. Then, feeling blindly for the spot with the tip of the blade, he drove the knife into the bear's side a little above and back from the shoulder. The brute gave out with one last agonized roar and reared up on his hind legs; then he stiffened and toppled over backwards, with Davy on top of him.

Davy staggered to his feet, whaling away at his dogs with both hands. "Tiger, Santwell, Rattler! Down!" He sent one of them flying with a well-placed kick. Spying Russell and his son on the edge of the clearing, he wiped a torn, bloody sleeve across his sweaty, dirt-streaked face and grinned, "If it hadn't been for those cussed dogs, I'd have squeezed him into b'ar jelly, corked it up in his skin, and taken it home for preserves!"

Not in the least ruffled by the incident, Davy went on to kill two more bears that day, and within two weeks he had upped the total to fifteen. Then, with more than enough fresh meat to last them on their journey, he and Russell cast off for New Orleans. They had almost reached Memphis when both boats piled up on an island in the middle of the Mississippi one dark night. Everyone aboard got safely on rafts except Davy, who was sleeping off a binge in the cabin of one of the boats. Before he could get out on deck, the boat rolled over on her side and began to sink in the channel. With the doorway completely submerged, he let the fast-rising water float him up to the level of the cabin windows, now face up in the river. He got his head and shoulders through one of the small apertures, braced his hands on the frame, and started to pull his body up. He was halfway through when his hips stuck fast. And no matter how hard he strained and squirmed, that was as far as he could get. Realizing that the boat would sink in a matter of minutes, he yelled for help as loudly as he could.

Fortunately, there were some other survivors nearby. They poled their raft over to him, and then, with six men yanking at Davy's arms and his head, a strange tug-of-war got under-way. They strained and they tugged for some time, making no appreciable headway, except to cause the window sash to groan and bend a little. But just when it seemed that Davy's head was bound to go under, there was a loud pop like a cork being pulled out of a champagne bottle, and they all went tumbling back in a heap with their prize on top of them, almost upsetting the raft. And not a moment too soon, either, for the only remaining sign of the boat was a stream of bubbles rising on the surface of the river.

It was a long time before any of the men forgot the comical sight of Colonel Crockett trying to make a show of dignity as he got to his feet. He was as naked as a plucked chicken, choice patches of hide had been scraped off his body, and wood splinters were sticking out of his butt like pin feathers. When he was finally able to stop laughing, George Russell said to Davy, "That politician's spread was nearly the death of you."

"That's the truth," Davy agreed. "I need to do man's work for a change. Soon as I get back home, I'm gonna chop me down some trees, build me another cabin, and plow up my land. I'm gonna hunt in the tall timber too, and sharpen up my shootin' eyes. I'll bag me a heap of b'ar or my name ain't Crockett."

That was the year Davy won the reputation of being "the world's greatest b'ar hunter." Every morning he would rise with the sun, fill his powder horn, stuff a handful of jerky in his pouch, and strike out into the hills of western Tennessee, with his hounds baying at his heels and his rifle slung across his shoulder. He never came home without a bearskin, even if it meant spending two or three days in the forest. This was one of the happiest times of his life, and wherever he went, the mountains echoed with the sound of his singing. He had a good, strong baritone voice, and he knew every backwoods ballad that had ever been sung. He had no mercy or respect for bears, little or big. He fought them barehanded in the cane, pulled them out of hollow tree trunks by the tail, and flushed them out of dark caves with a flaming torch and his knife clenched in his teeth. By the time the year was up, he had 105 bearskins piled in the storehouse behind his cabin, a record no other frontiersman ever came close to equaling.

Two years of hardy living helped Davy work the frustration out of his bones, but it didn't do anything to lessen his determination to win a seat in Congress. The 1826 elections found him electioneering with his customary cheerfulness and gusto against Colonel Alexander, the man who had beaten him the term before, and against the eminent General Will Arnold. His first campaign speech went over well enough, but when he was halfway through it, the usual cry went up, "Hey, Davy, we're thirsty!"

Davy grinned like a small boy and ran his hands idly through his empty pockets. Bear hunting had increased his popularity, but it hadn't lined his pocketbook. "Sure," he said in a casual voice, "let's mosey over to the shanty." Inwardly he said a prayer that the proprietor would be in a mood to extend him some credit. But as soon as they had stepped inside the makeshift shack, his heart sank into his moccasins. For the proprietor turned out to be a certain Job Snelling, a wizened, leather-faced old Yankee who had the reputation of being the meanest man in the county. To save people the trouble of testing him, he had a big sign hanging across the front of his bar that read: "Pay today and trust tomorrow."

When Davy called for drinks all around, Job pointed to the sign and waited wordlessly with his arms folded across his hollow chest. Grinning sheepishly, Davy turned his empty pockets inside out and made a feeble joke: "Stump speakers sometimes find themselves stumped." An uncertain titter ran through the crowd in back of him, but Job Snelling didn't find the remark humorous. He just tweaked one point of his greased handlebar mustache and regarded Davy coldly with his beady eyes. Delighting in his rival's predicament, another candidate stepped forward and stole some of Davy's thunder. "It's dry work listening to Colonel Crockett's speeches, ain't it? Who'll join me in a drink?"

Davy soon was as deserted as a politician with no patronage to bestow. Unless he could come up with some whisky fast, he knew he was in real danger of losing the election. So he slung old "Betsy" across his shoulder and headed into the woods; a half-hour later he was back with a fresh coonskin. He threw it on the bar and called for a quart. A coonskin was as good as cash any day, so Job Snelling smiled agreeably and set a quart of rum in front of Davy. It wasn't long before his constituents were flocking around him again, shouting, "Hurray for Crockett!"

When the bottle was empty, Davy marched out and mounted the stump to finish his speech. But he hadn't gotten very far when the voters began to show signs of thirsting for some more of Snelling's grog. Once more the procession trooped into the shanty with Davy calculating that the election—and the fate of the nation—depended upon his shooting another coon. He was just about to take up his rifle again when something on the floor caught his eye. Sticking out from between the logs that supported the bar was the tail of the coonskin he had traded to Job Snelling. Apparently Snelling had thrown it under the bar for safekeeping. Davy bent over and gave it a quick tug and it followed his hand "as natural as if I had been the rightful owner." He slapped it down on the counter, and Job, not realizing what had happened, set another bottle before him. Davy's constituents polished it off in considerable good humor; all of them were glad to see the stingy Snelling tricked. When the bottle was empty, they all followed Davy out to the stump to hear the rest of his speech.

Later on, when the voters were dry again, Davy took them back to the shanty, retrieved the same coonskin from between the logs, and traded it for another quart of rum. Before the day was over, he had secured ten quarts for the same skin. Of the ruse, Davy later wrote: "The joke secured me my election, for it circulated like smoke among my constituents, and they allowed with one accord that any man who could get the whip hand of Joe Snelling in fair trade could outwit old Nick himself, and was the real grit for them in Congress."

After the election was over, Davy sent Snelling the price of the rum, but the man refused it. He said that it did him good to be taken in occasionally; it served to keep him alert. Later Davy learned that Job had charged all the rum he had ordered against his opponent's account anyway.

Davy's congressional career was a spectacular one. He was coarse, he was profane, he was loud, and he was an incorrigible mimic. One of his favorite pastimes was to tell stag-party jokes in a thick Dutch brogue. His colleagues, with whom he was extremely popular, referred to him as the "Falstaff of the House," and the floor was always packed when one of his choice speeches was on the agenda. He literally kept the other representatives rolling in the aisles with outbursts like this:

". . . In one word I'm a screamer, and have got the

roughest racking horse, the prettiest sister, the surest rifle, and the ugliest dog in the district. I'm a little the savagest crittur you ever did see. My father can whip any man in Kentucky, and I can lick my father. I can outspeak any man on this floor, and give him two hours' start. I can run faster, dive deeper, stay longer under, and come out drier than any chap this side of the big swamp. . . ."

In one speech he said, "Congress allows lemonade to the members and has it charged under the head of stationery. I move also that whisky be allowed, under the item of fuel. . . ."

But those who thought Crockett was a naive clown soon found out he could argue them right off the floor when he got down to business. He remembered names, dates, facts, and the most intricate statistics with uncanny accuracy. Although his logic was often crude, it was always powerful. And people all over the country never ceased to marvel that this man, who could scarcely read or write, represented a constituency of over one hundred thousand votes. Davy got a big kick out of it himself. "I reckon I looked like a pretty cracklin' ever to get to Congress," he'd say with a sly grin. When his friend, the Hon. Mr. Verplanck, remarked that he didn't seem impressed after dining with President Adams at the White House, Davy laughed. "I was wild from the backwoods and didn't know nothing about eatin' dinner with the big folks. I had ate most of my dinners at a log in the woods. My constituents didn't benefit from me eatin' with the President."

It was inevitable that such a fervid champion of the common man would find his way into the camp of Andrew Jackson. The keynote of Jacksonian Democracy, a bastard offspring of the regular Democratic party, was government for the people, for the frontiersman, the farmer, the laborer, and the mechanic. It was hostile to vested interests, and it acclaimed individual freedom. Jackson's popularity almost took him to the Presidency in 1824, but he was beaten out when his arch rival Henry Clay threw his support to John Adams at the last minute. Davy Crockett liked Jackson's ideas and admired him as a man. After all, Old Hickory and he had fought side by side in the Creek War, and he knew the general was a rough, hard-riding, hard-cussing man of action. It was no problem at all for Jackson's backers to induce the fiery man from Tennessee to lend his oratorical talents to Old Hickory's cause when the 1828 elections got underway. In an address given in Raleigh, North Carolina, Davy brought a thunderous cheer from the crowd with the swashbuckling opening that became famous as Crockett's Brag:

"I'm the same Davy Crockett, fresh from the backwoods, half-horse, half-alligator, a little touched with snapping turtle. I can wade the Mississippi, leap the Ohio, ride upon a streak of lightning, and slip without a scratch down the honey locust tree; I can whip my weight in wildcats, and if any man pleases, he can throw in a panther for a ten dollar bill. I can hug a bear too close for comfort and whip any man opposed to Andrew Jackson!"

During his own campaign for re-election, Davy worked tirelessly for Jackson, and his efforts contributed greatly to the landslide popular vote that swept the general to the Presidency in 1829, the same year in which Crockett began his second term in the House of Representatives. But Davy Crockett's disillusionment with his hero was not long in coming. In his first address to Congress, Jackson, a ruthless expansionist, advocated that the Creeks, Cherokees, and other southern Indian tribes be removed from the rich land in the East, guaranteed them by "inviolable" treaties, to the wilderness west of the Mississippi, in direct violation of a Supreme Court decision which had upheld the treaties. Davy was horrified. Not only was it a flagrant disregard of human rights, he felt, but it was plain dishonest.

Up to this time he had been one of the President's "cronies," that select inner circle of party members to whom the President was accessible at all times—a practice that inspired Jackson's critics to comment that "the rabble enjoyed the run of the White House." Soon after the speech, Davy went storming in to see the President.

"We told those Injuns they could have that land," he insisted. "We even put it in writing. It's a bad enough thing when a man breaks his word, but when a big nation goes back on theirs, why, what are folks to think of us? The Indians are human beings, same as the rest of us. What's happened to all the fancy talk you use to spout about justice for the small man? Right now there ain't a smaller man in this country than the red man!"

"You're not being realistic, Colonel Crockett," the President said amicably. "The Indian is not a United States citizen, and he's got no more right to own land in the United States than the English or the French have to colonize in your old stamping grounds on the Obion River. And it's not as though we're going to steal the land from them. I'm perfectly willing to pay a fair price and have them transported to a new home west of the Mississippi." A note of self-righteousness crept into his voice. "After all, it's only right that the red man should have a nation of his own."

But there was no common ground for a compromise between two men of such indomitable purpose and opposing viewpoints. Finally Andrew Jackson grew impatient, "Look, Crockett, I've had just about all the impudence I'm going to take. Either you fall in line with the rest of the party or you'll have to take the consequences. It will mean political suicide."

"I'll have to take that chance," Davy said solemnly.

"You'll live to regret this rashness," the President said. "You're popular with the people, and there's no telling how far you could have gone in politics with a little good judgment and the party behind you."

Davy laughed confidently. "As long as the people are behind me, I won't worry about what you or the party think about me, General."

Jackson shook his head sadly. "Man is a fickle creature, Davy. You'll find that out."

In the next few years, Davy learned this bitter lesson all too well. His violent opposition to Jackson, plus the fact that he was an outspoken admirer of Henry Clay and the United States Bank, completely alienated him from the Democratic

Party. He was branded a conservative, although nothing could have been further from the truth. Contemptuous of the fact that Old Hickory was the hero of the West, Davy carried his private war with the administration into the thick of the 1831 elections. It was too big a handicap, even for a man of his stature in Tennessee. In a close race he lost out by seventy votes. The people had let him down, but he wasn't beaten. Attributing his defeat to the fact that he had been out of touch with his constituents for too long a period, he resolved to tour the state and make speeches in an attempt to justify his attitude toward Jackson.

In between these appeals to his constituents, Davy found time to work on his memoirs and bring his journals up to date. Only ten years after he had made his first serious effort to improve his literacy, he was able to write proficient and readable prose. When Davy announced his intention to run for Congress again in the 1833 elections, the Democrats were amused. As far as Washington was concerned, the irrepressible backwoodsman was safely "dead and buried." No one was more surprised than President Jackson when the votes were counted and Davy was sent back to his old seat in the House, where he took swipes at Old Hickory with undiminished vigor.

In his first speech, Davy rolled back his cuffs and stretched his arms above his head and bellowed, "I'm back, gentlemen, and see, there ain't no handcuffs on me!" He ripped his shirt open. "I ain't wearing no collar, either, with a tag that says, *My Dog—Andy Jackson.*" His remarkable comeback, waged singlehandedly, and uphill all the way, was a severe jolt to the Democrats, but it also earned their grudging respect.

Jackson swore loudly, "Damn it, if he'd only work for us, he could become the next President. We'll give him one more chance, gentlemen."

The party bigwigs tried to make a deal with Davy. "We've got to start thinking about bringing along a man for the '38 Presidential election," they told him. "You're Andrew Jackson's personal choice. You're strong, you're popular with the people. We don't think you can miss . . . if . . ."

Davy grinned. "If I knuckle down to Andy Jackson. Is that it, gentlemen?"

"We're only asking a reasonable amount of cooperation, Colonel. Be sensible, man. What do you hope to gain by fighting your own party?"

"I'd rather keep conscience with an empty purse than a bad opinion of myself with a full one."

"You know what that means, don't you? We'll step on you like we would a rattlesnake. Andy Jackson will personally campaign against you in your own district in the next election, if he has to. This time you'll be through for good!"

Davy shrugged. "You can extend my thanks to Andy Jackson for his generous offer, but I'm sorry, gentlemen. I will pledge myself to no administration. I had rather be politically damned than hypocritically immortalized. If I don't, I wish I may be shot." He got up and turned his back on them.

From that point on, however, the horse sense that had taken Davy Crockett over so many hurdles began to fail him. Repugnant as the offer of the Jacksonians was to him, it could hardly help but flatter him. The party had come to him and practically begged him to stand for President. Even though he was one man, standing alone, they had acted as if they were afraid of him. Maybe they thought he could do it without their help, he told himself—and why not?

On April 25, 1834, Davy left Washington on a tour of the Northeast, "to become a better legislator." There was considerable speculation among the loyal constituents, who had defied Jackson to rally around him in the last election, about Colonel Crockett's motives in visiting the big metropolitan cities when he should have been watching out for their interests in Congress.

Generally speaking, Davy's tour was a singular triumph. In Louisville, Baltimore, Pittsburgh, Cincinnati, wherever he went, thousands turned out to greet him and laugh at his shrewd comments on life and national affairs. In his most extravagant moments he had never imagined that his fame was so widespread. He was wined and dined in royal style, feted by the newspapers and the city officials. Never did a man make so much progress in so few months. Inevitably, the sophistications of big city life began to rub off on him. He grew to like the feel and cut of tailored clothes, the polish of fine boots, the luxury of the best hotel suites, and the taste of continental food and liquor. But his unerring showmanship never let him forget that his audience expected to be entertained. He liked to appear on the speaker's platform in his old buckskins and moccasins, with the old coon hat pushed back on his head.

In Philadelphia he was presented with an elegant rifle, made especially for him by the Colt people, and he made a big show of pointing it around the hall, aiming at visiting dignitaries. He impressed on them that he was a child of nature, when he spoke of the loneliness of the big city. "If anyone has a grand idea of himself, of his own importance, let him go to a city, and he will find that he is not higher valued than a coonskin." He won over New York entirely, but he ran into trouble in New Jersey when he was invited to test his marksmanship against the state champion. It was an awkward situation, for he hadn't fired a rifle in over a year, and from what he had seen of the Jersey man's shooting, he knew he would have had a rough time beating him even when his eye was at its best. But to refuse the challenge was unthinkable, for the legends that had been circulating for years had exaggerated his skill with a rifle beyond all proportion. Knowing that only a miracle could save his face, Davy stepped up to the firing line. He spit on his thumb, wet his sights carefully, took a deep breath, and squinted down the barrel of his rifle at the paper target tacked up on a board about one hundred yards away. He squeezed the trigger and felt the bullet kick off with a loud crack. There was a tense moment as the judge stepped out from behind a big tree at the end of the range and inspected the target. Then he cupped his hands to his mouth and shouted, "Bull's-eye!" Davy breathed an inaudible sigh of relief as the crowd in back of him let out a loud cheer. He stepped back, and with a magnificent flourish relinquished the firing line to his opponent.

The New Jersey champion was a tall, emaciated fellow with a long, impassive horse face. Hardly bothering to aim, he whipped off his shot, and again the cry went up from the judge, "Bull's-eye!"

As was the custom, the Jersey man took his turn first in the second round. After the fellow shot, Davy called "time," and everybody walked down to the far end of the field to inspect the targets. Davy bit his lip when he saw two holes overlapping one another on the Jerseyman's target, both within the small circumference of the bull's-eye. A murmur of admiration went up from the crowd. Davy scooped out a handful of dirt from the pock-marked backwall and idly sifted it through his fingers. Then he leaned up against the board with one hand resting carelessly across his own target paper. "That's mighty fine shooting, son," he said. "I wouldn't be surprised if you got me beat for fair." He winked at the crowd around him as if sharing some huge joke with them, and turned back to the firing line. As he was preparing to shoot, he was pleased to hear a few of his backers still taking bets on him.

Davy made a real production of his next turn, scowling and cocking his head this way and that to examine the target. When he finally brought the rifle to his shoulder, he paused dramatically for several seconds before he squeezed off the shot. There was a disappointed groan from the spectators as the judge announced in an incredulous tone that Davy's second shot had missed the target completely! Again there was a mass migration to the other end of the field, where the town officials, badly embarrassed for Colonel Crockett's sake, stood about gawkily, scuffling their feet in the dirt and inventing outlandish reasons to excuse his lapse. But there was no sign of humiliation on Davy's face.

"Stand aside and let me look," he said cheerfully. He stepped up to the target and took his knife out of its sheath. Standing aside to afford everyone an unobstructed view, he began to dig into the bull's eye of his target. A spent ball fell out on the ground. He dug a little more. A second ball dropped out into the dirt. There was the hiss of a hundred breaths being exhaled in wonder.

Davy turned to the visibly shaken Jersey champion. "There it is. Be there no snakes in the world if it hasn't followed the very track of the other."

Much later, in his memoirs, Davy explained the feat. Employing a little sleight-of-hand, he had picked up a spent bullet on his first visit to the target and jammed it into the hole made by his first shot. Then he had deliberately shot past the target on his second try, setting up the dramatic "discovery."

The voters in his own district followed the progress of Davy Crockett's triumphant march through the North and the East with growing concern and a little sadness. The two-fisted, hard-drinking hero who had captivated them with his jokes and stories of Indian fighting and bear hunting, who had always been friend and brother to the frontier people, was fast fading in their eyes. When Davy returned to Tennessee, obviously pleased by his triumph and looking, in his fine clothes, like a gentleman who had just stepped out of an English drawing room, their worst suspicions were confirmed. Davy confidently expected to sweep unresisted through the 1834 elections to another term in Congress, after which he intended to get down to the serious business of grooming himself for the Presidency. He doffed his city duds for the old buckskins and coon hat, mounted the stump, told the same boisterous stories and jokes, swaggered into the shanties, and bought all the whisky his constituents could drink. But it wasn't quite the same, somehow. All the mannerisms which had once held so much appeal for the backwoods people now seemed as unnatural as the cheap affectations of a petty politician who went around kissing babies and then, surreptitiously, wiped his mouth and spit in the bushes. The whole district was solidly behind President Jackson and the man he was backing for the office. That year Davy suffered an overwhelming defeat at the polls. When his friends tried to console him, he smiled bitterly. "It ain't the first time in my life I discovered too late that I have a far better opinion of myself than other folks have." Then, in a lighter mood, he added. "Anyway, it's all for the best. I've had about all I can stomach of those long-winded politicians. No one who ain't tried can imagine what hard work it is to listen to those fellows talk."

But now the old life held nothing but dissatisfaction for him. The bear hunts were monotonous, the forest had lost its charm, the physical demands of frontier living were a drudgery. Davy's whole existence seemed empty and meaningless. The old restlessness closed in on him tighter and tighter until, finally, one day he said to his wife, "I think I may go down to Texas and have a look around."

She sat down heavily. "I was just beginning to think we could settle down and live out the rest of our lives peacefully like other folks, now that this Washington business is over."

"I ain't ready for a rockin' chair yet by a long shot," Davy said. He removed Betsy from pegs above the fireplace and blew the dust off the barrel.

"What are you going to do in Texas? That's a wild place these days. Aren't the people there fighting with the Mexicans?"

Davy picked up a rag and ran it up and down the length of the rifle. "That's just it. There's big things brewing in Texas. The way I see it, those settlers are going to break away from Mexico and form a sovereign state of their own."

"Nonsense! What chance do a handful of settlers have against the whole Mexican Army?"

"They won't be alone, you can take my word for it. There's plenty in this country who're willing to back 'em up to the hilt. That's a big rich territory down there. It wouldn't hurt the government's feelings if they came into the Union."

"But how does all this concern you, Davy?"

Daxy fixed a patch to the end of his ramrod and jammed it into the barrel of the rifle. "Once our boys lick the Mexicans, they're going to need experienced men to help 'em set up a government."

"So that's it!" She pushed back her chair abruptly and stood up with her hands on her hips. "Davy Crockett, you're getting to sound just like all the other politicians. You're power mad!"

"That ain't fair." He avoided her eyes. "But as long as there's work to be done in this country, I don't aim to sit back and leave all the doin' to others."

"You may fool yourself with that rot, but you're not fooling me any. There's still plenty of work to be done right here in Tennessee for those who want to do it."

Davy slammed the rifle down on the table and walked over to the fireplace. He kicked the bricks angrily. "It appears my services ain't no longer appreciated in this state. I worked and fought for these people, and what did I get for my trouble? They helped Andy Jackson knife me in the back."

"Are you sure of that?" She took a bowl of peas down from the shelf, sat down at the table again, and began to shell them into her apron. "You always used to say, Davy, that it might be easy for a slippery politician to pull the wool over the eyes of city folks, but that a backwoodsman had too much horse sense to believe their lies."

Davy mumbled something unintelligible.

"I think you were right, Davy," she went on determinedly. "I think they can recognize a politician even if he disguises himself in a coonskin hat."

"I don't have to listen to that kind of talk," Davy roared, clapping both hands down on the mantel so hard it shook. He whirled, grabbed his gun off the table, and went out into the backyard. Half an hour later Davy came back into the house, walked up quietly behind his wife at the stove, and put his arms around her. "I could bite off my tongue for raisin' my voice to you. Maybe you're right about me. But when a man sets out to cut the big figure, halfway measures don't count nohow. I got this thing in my blood, and I got to settle it one way or the other."

She patted his arm without turning around. "I know, Davy, and I guess I wouldn't want you to be any different. Promise me one thing, though. Don't play the politician any more. Just be yourself."

Davy laughed. "It ain't every man has a wife who's pretty,

and clever too. I'll remember what you said. What's more, I promise you if this Texas business doesn't strike me right, I'll come home for good."

A note of underlying sadness was in the air when Davy left home the next day. His wife and daughters sniffled when they kissed him good-bye, and his sons gripped his hand a little tighter and held on to it a little longer than usual. As his horse rounded a bend in the trail and the house slipped out of sight, a lump formed in his own throat, and he had to swallow a few times to clear it. A little later he unstrapped the old guitar from his saddlebag and began to sing:

> *Farewell to the mountains whose mazes to me*
> *Were more beautiful by far than Eden could be,*
> *No fruit was forbidden, but Nature has spread,*
> *Her bountiful board and her children were fed.*
> *The home I forsake where my offspring arose.*
> *The graves I forsake where my loved ones repose.*
> *The home I redeemed from the savage and wild,*
> *The house I have loved as a father his child,*
> *The corn that I planted, the fields that I cleared,*
> *The cabins I built and the flocks that I reared,*
> *The wife of my bosom, Farewell to ye all,*
> *In the land of the stranger I rise or I fall.*

The town of Bexar was situated about 140 miles from the Gulf of Mexico on the San Antonio River. The population numbered about twelve hundred, mostly Mexicans. In 1721, Spain established a military outpost there because the land was good and there was plenty of water. Across the river from the town they built a mission which they called "Alamo," for the cottonwood trees which grew around it. On December 10, 1835, the rebel Texans captured Bexar from the Mexicans and converted the Alamo, with its thick eight-foot walls, into a fort. A small garrison was established there, under the command of Colonel Travis. What they lacked in numbers, the men of the Alamo made up for in courage and spirit.

The cause of Texas independence attracted, for the most part, reckless men without responsibilities who had little or nothing to lose—escaped convicts, wanted murderers, run-away slaves, vagabonds, soldiers of fortune, and adventurers. Among the more notable adventurers who drifted into the Alamo were Jim Bowie and Davy Crockett. The swashbuckling atmosphere of the fort was like a drug to Davy's lagging spirits. He relished the atmosphere of mounting tension, the ever-present danger, the comradeship, the laughter.

A hero to the Texans even before he joined them, Davy won their hearts completely with his funny stories, his earthy humor, and his sharp tongue. When he first saw Jim Bowie slashing away at a side of beef with his famous "Bowie" knife, Davy whistled, "That weapon's enough to give a man with a squeamish stomach the colic. You might tickle a feller's ribs a long time with that little instrument before you'd make him laugh, Jim." The unwashed buckskins and coon hat began to feel comfortable on Davy once more, and the fluency which public life had lent to his speech gave way completely to the old backwoods vernacular. Furthermore, Davy was soon out-shooting the best riflemen in the fort. He could sit up all night around the campfire and match the younger men drink for drink, and then slip away with them before dawn into the village and "outamour" them with the senoritas.

Late in February, the report came in that Santa Anna's army was marching on the Alamo, and everyone knew that the time for having fun was over. The ponderous gates were shut and barred, and an immense flag was unfurled over the battlement. The flag had thirteen stripes and a big five-pointed white star with a letter at each point spelling out Texas. Santa Anna's men moved across the plains like an army of ants, swarming about the Alamo on all sides—infantry, cavalry, and artillery, their banners waving sinuously in the breeze, their bugles blaring a challenge at the beleaguered little garrison. Colonel Travis answered a demand for unconditional sur-render with a defiant cannon shot. Then the Mexicans raised their traditional blood-red banner—to signify that there would be no mercy shown to anyone in the fort—and the siege got underway on February 24.

That night Colonel Travis sent a messenger through the Mexican lines to Goliad, where a detachment of Texas Army regulars was stationed. "It's a five-day march," he told his men. "But we've got enough food and water for a week, and powder and shot for twice that time. We can make it until help comes, boys." The defenders manning the parapet grinned and slapped one another confidently. Davy waved his fist in the direction of the Mexican lines. "They'll find they have to do with men who will never lay down their arms as long as they can stand on their legs."

Under cover of darkness, Santa Anna forged a ring of steel around the Alamo. His field cannon moved up to within 350 yards of the walls, and at daybreak opened up a sporadic bombardment of the fort. Davy Crockett, wrapped up in his blanket, was snoozing peacefully with his back propped against the battlement when the first barrage crashed into the wall behind him. The shock wave lifted him a good six inches into the air, then dropped him back on the stone with a thud that rattled his teeth. Bleary-eyed and swearing loudly, he staggered to his feet and peered out through a slit in the parapet. Framed in the opening was a Mexican cannon, its crew bustling about the job of reloading.

"Ain't those bastards got better sense than to wake a man up this early in the morning?" Davy grumbled to the man beside him. "I guess I gotta teach 'em some manners." He pulled the cork from his powder horn with his teeth and tipped some powder into the muzzle of his rifle. Tight-lipped and narrow-eyed, he braced himself on the ledge of the parapet and trained old "Betsy" on the Mexican artillerymen. They didn't show up much bigger than grasshoppers in his sights. As the gunner prepared to touch a firebrand to the fuse, Davy squeezed the trigger. The gunner clutched his chest and toppled forward across the cannon. Davy reloaded quickly as the Mexicans lifted the body of their comrade off the gun. Another member of the crew bent over to snatch a lighted firebrand from the bucket at his feet, but as he straightened up, the top of his head was blasted off.

Down the line from Davy, a man stepped away from the

wall and shouted, "Nice shooting, Crockett! But I got a couple of cartwheels that says I get more of the skunks today than you do!"

Davy grinned as he reloaded. "You're on, Bee-keeper." The big jolly redhead, who got his nickname from his taste for honey, had been the only man to give Davy any serious competition in the daily target practice at the fort. In less than five minutes, Davy had picked off the remaining three members of the Mexican gun crew. He surveyed the five bodies sprawled grotesquely in the sand about the silent cannon and spit over the wall. "Now I think I'll mosey down and have my breakfast and bitters. It'll give the Bee-keeper a chance to catch up." He planted a wet kiss on the barrel of his rifle. "Ouch! I never did see a gal get as hot as you, Betsy!"

But as the siege moved into the second week, the picnic-holiday frame of mind of the little garrison became more subdued. Food and water were almost gone, and ammunition and powder were running low. Faces were lean, pinched, and lined with strain; eyes were hollow and bloodshot from lack of rest. Many of the men caught dysentery drinking from a contaminated well. Colonel Bowie had come down with a fever and was too weak to get out of his bed in the chapel. As the casualties increased, the ranks on the ramparts thinned out dangerously. But hunger, thirst, sickness, and the ever-mounting peril only made the defenders of the Alamo more belligerent. A hint of their temper can be discovered in one of the last entries in Davy Crockett's diary. "For just one shot at that rascal Santa Anna, I would bargain to break my 'Betsy' and never pull a trigger again. My name's not Davy Crockett if I wouldn't get glory enough to appease my stomach for the remainder of my life."

Every morning, Colonel Travis would scan the flat circle of the horizon hopefully. "It won't be long now. First you'll see a cloud of dust like a storm might kick up. Then, the next thing you know, the whole Texas Army will come charging across that damned prairie." At first, the men believed him, and every time an eddy of dust churned up on the desert, it aroused excited speculation. But repeated woodenly, day after day, the words became a barren joke, and even Colonel Travis at length ceased to believe them.

Meanwhile, the call for help from the Alamo had put the commander at Goliad in a bad spot. Against the powerful Mexican Army, the only thing the pitiful handful of regulars could hope to accomplish was their own destruction. The alert went out all over Texas for volunteers to rally to the emergency. But disorganization and dissension among the insurgents occasioned all kinds of delays. And while they were bickering with each other and making patriotic speeches, the Alamo fell.

On the night of March 5, Davy Crocket made the final entry in his diary: "Poop, pop, poop, boom, boom, boom throughout the day. No time for memorandums now. Go ahead! Liberty and independence forever."

At daybreak on the sixth of March, three thousand Mexican troopers stormed the Alamo in a mass assault. A swath of bloodstained sand widened slowly around the base of the wall as dozens writhed and died under the last savage salvos from the fort. But hundreds more took their places. As Santa Anna's soldiers swarmed over the parapet, the defenders met them with clubs, knives, hatchets, and fists, and drove them off time after time. But at last the battlements were engulfed in a tidal wave of Mexicans, who cut down the Texans ruthlessly and methodically, with pistols, bayonets, and slashing sabers, until only six were left. Impressed with the courage of the survivors, Mexican General Castrilla ordered his men to take them alive.

From his bed, Jim Bowie waged a one-man war against a squad of soldiers who had broken into the chapel. He fought them with two pistols, then in hand-to-hand combat with his knife, before they nailed him to his wooden cot with their bayonets. Six Mexicans died with him.

Outside on the battlements, Davy Crockett, a Bowie knife clenched in his teeth, was holding off a company of Mexicans in an angle of the wall. Swinging his rifle like a club, he bashed in heads left and right. When the rifle was shattered and twisted, he threw it aside and went at them with his knife. Before they were able to pin his arms to the wall, there was a ring of dead men around him.

General Castrilla hinted to the six prisoners that a demonstration of humility might induce Santa Anna to spare their lives. But when they were lined up before the paunchy, arrogant little Mexican leader, Davy spat insolently at his feet between his polished boots. "So you're Santy Anna." His eyes traveled contemptuously over the rows of medals and ribbons decking the tight-fitting tunic. Then, without warning, he leaped past the guard and reached for Santa Anna's throat. Pistols barked and swords flashed in the sunlight.

Santa Anna dug his toe experimentally into the still form sprawled out at his feet and raised heavily-lidded eyes to General Castrilla. "A brave man," he said simply. "You will dispose of the others now, please." He made a neat military about-face and walked away. Davy Crockett's great heart had stopped beating; his legend had just begun.

The Saga of Sam Houston

By IRV GOODMAN

A hard drinker and a harder fighter, he tamed Indians, the Wild West, and the ladies. Soldier, statesman, and empire builder, he was jack-of-all trades and master of all.

Andrew Jackson, a practical man, once gave some advice on dueling to his young friend, Sam Houston. It was just before Houston was to conduct a matched-pistols-at-dawn bit of business with a professional duelist, sitting in for the original culprit who was loud-mouthed, but no gentleman.

"Sam," Old Hickory told the young man, "bite a bullet between your teeth. It will steady your hand."

It was good advice from a man who knew, and for almost any duelist it would have been a comforting edge. For Sam Houston, however, it was like telling Samson how to hit a

Philistine in the mouth. Sam Houston came to this world ready and enormously able—and that's the way he left it. Name the sport, Sam could handle it. War or peace, world diplomacy or back-alley politics, he was a man who needed no instruction and very little road work. If it is true that life on the frontier was a struggle between the quick and the dead, Sam was a jack rabbit. Whiskey, women, Indians—Sam knew how to deal with them. He was a jack-of-all-trades and master of all.

But Sam Houston had one thing above everything else, and that was principle. He failed in his two chances at the Presidency of the United States because he would rather be right than be President. It was a hell of a stand to take in the hothanded young America of the last century, a century of hungry young men in a hungry young country. But America belonged to Houston as much as it did to any man—and he clung to it as if it would fall apart if he let go. It might have, at that, if it hadn't been for Sam and a few others of his breed.

Sam Houston was born on March 2, 1793, at a place called Timber Ridge Church in Virginia. When he was fourteen, his mother crossed the Alleghenies in a five-horse team and a new wagon and took her nine children to the foothills of the Great Smoky Mountains. It was there that Sam's father had selected 419 acres of rich land for farming just before he died.

The new land excited Sam—until the new house was built and he was put to work with the rest of the family clearing the land. When there were chores to do, Sam would take off, find a shady tree near a cool spring, and settle down with his *Iliad*. He read the ballads of the Trojan War so constantly in those days that he committed almost all of the book to memory. His mother couldn't bring herself to scold her handsome and shiftless son, but his older brothers, who had to do his work, could and did. A family council was finally held, and it was unanimously agreed that Sam was no farmer. The brothers put him behind the counter of a store which they owned in town. But jockeying bolts of yarn was worse than jockeying a plow horse. Sam ran away.

He swam across the Tennessee River and joined a tribe of Cherokee Indians. It was wild living and he loved it. Those days gave Sam a profound understanding of the character of the red man. Probably no man in American history understood the Indians better or handled them more effectively.

After a few months, his brothers found him and took him home. But it wasn't long before Sam took off again. This time, he went to the wigwam of the Cherokee chief, Oo-loo-te-ka, who adopted him as his son. Oo-loo-te-ka named Sam, Co-lon-neh (The Raven), and taught him the Cherokee language. The hunters of the tribe took him out and taught him the ways of the wilderness. From the chiefs around the council fire, Sam picked up the art of oratory, as he listened to them telling their wonderful stories of the folklore of the Cherokee Nation. He, in turn, told them stories from the *Iliad*. From the handsome girls of the village, he learned about love and the ways of the heart. And from these Indian days, much of Sam's personality was molded—his hatred of barter, his disregard for money, his almost childish vanity, his love of theatrics, and his loud dress.

For three years, Sam lived with the peaceful Cherokee. Once in a while, when he wanted clothing or needed money to buy a gift for a favored girl, he would visit his mother. When he went heavily into debt buying gifts for too many girls, he came back to open a country school. (He had had no more than six months of formal schooling himself.) Each pupil paid eight dollars for the semester; one-third in cash, one-third in corn, and one-third in cotton cloth. After the first term, Sam was able to pay his debts and he closed the school. But before he could return to the peaceful life of the Cherokees, he was caught up in the War of 1812.

When Sam's mother sent him off to this, his first war, he was twenty. She said to this restless son: "Here, take this musket and never disgrace it. I would rather all my sons should fill one honorable grave than that one of them should turn his back to save his life. This door, my son, is eternally shut against cowards." Then she placed on his finger a plain gold ring which he wore until his death many, many years later. Engraved on the ring was the single word—"Honor."

Sam marched off to the war, but it wasn't ready for him. He had made the mistake of joining the regulars, and he was required to take military training. He was assigned to the Seventh Infantry at Knoxville, and thirty days later, he was a drill sergeant. Three months later, he was an ensign (one rank lower than second lieutenant at the time). He trained for a year, and then, finally, was sent to fight the Creek Indians, who had gone over to the British. Tecumseh, a brigadier general in the British Army, had been sent to stir up trouble among the Creeks, who were already angry with the white men for failing to keep a promise—a familiar story in those days. Tecumseh did his job well; the Red Stick (war club) hung in the square of the Creek encampment, and the British rushed in arms.

General Andrew Jackson, busy making a name for himself, went after them, but he had only militiamen, who were used to leaving the army whenever they felt like it. So it was a great relief to Jackson when a regiment of regular army men joined him. Among the reinforcements was platoon leader Sam Houston, taut and quivering with eagerness to fight.

Jackson met the Creeks at Horseshoe Bend, a peninsula on the Tallapoosa River, where a thousand warriors had prepared for a single mighty struggle. They had put up a breastwork of heavy pine logs at the opening to the Bend, and although Jackson deployed his troops masterfully, surrounding the peninsula and leaving no escape route, it was a difficult battle to pursue. The Creeks were dug in deep, and Jackson's two artillery pieces had no effect on the breastworks.

There was no choice but to storm the ramparts. On the order to charge, a major leaped on the logs and was hit. The next man over was Ensign Houston, breathless, brave, and determined to achieve military fame. Waving his sword, Sam scaled the breastworks. He stood at the top for a moment and called to his platoon to follow, and then, uttering a fearful cry, he leaped down among the Indians. The Creeks were upon him, as Sam knew they would be, and he slashed away ferociously with his sword. Moments later, a barbed arrow, fired at almost point-blank range, dug deep into his thigh. Sam kept his feet, fighting off the Indians until his men reached him. Now that the dent had been made, the soldiers poured through. Sam dropped to the ground and tried to remove the arrow, but it wouldn't come loose.

A lieutenant came by, and Sam called to him: "Pull out this damn arrow!" The lieutenant, using care instead of strength, tugged gently at the shaft. "Damn it, pull!" Sam screamed. He was mad with pain. Again the lieutenant fumbled with the arrow and the pain grew worse. "Try again, man!" Sam ordered. He drew his pistol and said in a thick voice, "If you don't pull it out, I'll kill you!" The lieutenant took hold of the shaft, shut his eyes to the sight, and pulled with all his strength. The arrow came out, tearing the flesh and unleashing a gush of blood. Sam dragged himself back across the breastworks, found a surgeon, and had the wound dressed. Then he sat down to rest.

General Jackson came by and recognized him. "Back to the rear, Ensign," Jackson ordered.

"General," Sam pleaded, "I'm able to walk. Let me join my men."

"No," Jackson said firmly. "I don't want you coming across those outworks. Is that understood?" Sam grumbled something unintelligible, and the general rode away.

But Sam Houston had fame to chase. When the crusty general was out of sight, he scrambled over the breastworks and rejoined his troop.

The battle wasn't going well. The Creeks had been told that the Great Spirit had assured their ultimate victory, and they wouldn't surrender. The battle had become a hand-to-hand struggle with swords and tomahawks clashing. The Indians had taken a fearsome loss—hundreds killed, countless others wounded or drowned trying to swim the river. One party of them had taken to a part of the breastworks built over a ravine, like the roof of a house, with narrow portholes to fire through at the attacking soldiers. Only a frontal assault could dislodge them from their position.

Jackson called for a company of volunteers, but the lines stood still. (There is a bit of protocol involved here. When the call is made for a company, it is customary for the company commander to volunteer, not a subordinate.) Sam was sick with nervousness as he waited for some captain to step forward and offer his company. He waited perhaps ten seconds. Then, ignoring protocol completely, he dashed for the ravine, calling to his platoon to follow. His men, sensible soldiers, didn't move. Sam was desperate; he *had* to make that assault. He grabbed a musket from one of his men and, at gunpoint, ordered them to follow him.

Sam charged directly into the murderous fusillade. Just five yards from the portholes, he stopped to rally his men for the final assault. As he did, he took a rifle ball in his right shoulder. His musket fell to the ground. He started in again, and another rifle ball caught his shoulder, this time shattering it. Still standing, Sam turned and begged his men to follow him. Instead, they dropped to the ground and began crawling back to the main body of troops. Alone and frustrated, unable to attack single-handed, Sam climbed back to the ravine, somehow avoiding the concentration of firepower exploding all around him. Once beyond rifle range, he sank to the earth, bleeding and crying tears of blind frustration.

Now Jackson showed his military talents; he had flaming arrows fired into the breastworks. The burning logs smoked out the last of the Indians, and the Creek insurrection was over.

After the battle, searchers found Houston, barely breathing, among the dead that filled the ravine. The dying man was taken from the field and turned over to a surgeon in the rear camp. The doctor was able to extract one of the balls from his shoulder, but refused to probe for the other. It was useless torture for the young man, he said, since he couldn't possibly survive the night.

All that night, Sam lay on the damp earth ("as soldiers will who war in the wilderness," he said later), alone and unattended. When he was still alive in the morning, he was placed on a litter and carried seventy miles to Fort Williams. For weeks, he was kept there, untreated but refusing to die. Finally he was brought, on a crude litter, through the forests of northern Alabama, across Tennessee, and to the doorstep of his mother—to die in his own bed. His mother, looking at the son who had reaped honor and still had a rifle ball inside his shoulder, recognized him only because "the eyes looked like my son."

Yet, somehow this remarkable young man refused to die. He survived, and, after a while, even began to improve. When he was able to ride, Sam headed for New Orleans. The war was still on, and the hunger for battle growled inside him. But he was too late. Andy Jackson won his glorious victory at New Orleans before Sam could get there. It was an immense disappointment to the young soldier.

With peace, the Army was reduced, but through the intervention of General Jackson, Houston was retained in service and promoted to second lieutenant. Jackson wanted Sam because there was trouble with the Indians, due partly to the general's aim to seize Florida. Young Houston had a lot of influence with the Indians, and Jackson felt he could trust him. Sam's help was invaluable, mainly because he was able to convince his foster father, Oo-loo-te-ka, to go west with the other tribes that were being moved out of eastern Tennessee.

During these negotiations, Houston traveled to Washington with a delegation of chiefs to establish new boundary lines and settle the question of reparations. It was here he ran into trouble with John C. Calhoun, then Secretary of War. Sam, dressed in breechcloth and blanket to show his friendship to the Indians, was received by Calhoun. When the meeting ended, Calhoun asked the young lieutenant to stay.

"It seems to me," the Secretary said, "a raw impertinence for a soldier to call upon a member of the Cabinet dressed as an Indian. I think it frightfully rude, sir."

"But, sir . . ." Sam started to answer.

"Never mind any explanations," the Secretary snapped. "Your affectation is an insult. That is all."

Sam was still angry when he left Washington. Calhoun, the next day, tried to accuse him of slave smuggling, but Sam stopped that quickly and received a forced apology. But

Calhoun had made a dedicated enemy, who years later would stop him from becoming President. Sam had wanted a military career, but not if it meant enduring insults and injury. On May 18, 1818, he resigned from the Army and went to Nashville.

He became a lawyer because it seemed to be the only thing open to him. He read a few of the standard works and within six months passed the bar examination. The law proved an ideal profession for Sam. A lawyer who hung out his shingle on the frontier didn't need the vast detail of the law. He needed to be eloquent, brave, and willing to fight in a courtroom on more than points of law. Young Houston lacked none of this.

He opened his first office in Lebanon, thirty miles from Nashville. His office rent was one dollar a month, a tavernkeeper trusted him for his room and board, and town merchants gave him clothing suitable for a counselor-at-law. But Sam wasn't a struggling young lawyer for long. His war record and his oversized personality brought him many clients. And Andy Jackson, who was busy building a political machine reaching from Tennessee to Washington, helped.

Sam moved swiftly up the political ladder. In 1819, he was elected prosecuting attorney for the Nashville district and was appointed an adjutant-general. In 1821, he was elected major general of the Tennessee militia. The next year, Jackson arranged to have him nominated for Congress, and Sam won easily. He ran unopposed.

It was only five years since he had left the Army, disillusioned and angry, and here he was, thirty years old, a major general, a congressman, and the close friend of the most popular man in the country. He went to Washington happy, ambitious, and thoroughly self-confident. "Now that I am a member of Congress," he said, "I will show Mr. Calhoun that I haven't forgotten his insult." As the first assault of a campaign that lasted many years, Sam sent Calhoun a bill for his transportation costs to get to Washington. It was something congressmen didn't do, and Calhoun objected; but he paid —thirty-six dollars.

In the Presidential election of 1824, Jackson polled the most popular votes, but because no candidate—there were four—had a majority, the election was thrown into the House of Representatives, where Houston lobbied mightily for his friend. But John Quincy Adams won. And Jackson and his friends began preparing for the campaign of 1828. One of the jobs was to keep the governorship of Tennessee. So Sam was put up.

He ran an unprecedented campaign that included log-rolling contests, barn-raising, horse races, and barbecues. Sam, it became apparent, had been preparing for years for just such a campaign. No Boss Crump or Tammany Hall ever fed and feted the electorate better. On Election Day, with everything secure, Sam toured the polling places of Nashville on a dapple-gray horse. He wore a bell-crowned black beaver hat, a ruffled shirt, a black satin vest, shining black trousers, an Indian hunting shirt with a beaded sash. He was the dandy of Nashville, and Nashville was a dandy place for Sam Houston.

At a banquet, after Sam had been elected, when the ladies had retired, a toast was given in the name of the ladies to Houston: "We pledge you, General, that the ladies will not forget the brave."

They did not. Sam romanced every eligible and attractive woman in the city. It was high living, but it had its problems. After Jackson won the Presidency in 1828, Sam became that much more important. He was Old Hickory's boy, and his future was bright. But he was thirty-five years old and still a bachelor. It didn't look right for a fellow with the look of a Presidential candidate to live as high as Sam was living. The political advice of the boys who always manage these things was—marry and settle down.

It wasn't a difficult problem to handle. Sam was already in love—with an eighteen-year-old beauty with blue eyes and yellow hair. His political friends approved; she was of a good Tennessee family. Her name was Eliza Allen. Formerly, Sam had been an adult confidant to her, but lately he had noticed that she had grown into womanhood. Suddenly, he became a persuasive pursuer. Eliza was bewildered and undoubtedly impressed. Big Sam Houston was a choice catch in any season, and a handsome devil to boot. He swept her off her feet, or so it seemed, and in January of 1829, they were married. Eliza moved into Sam's handsome apartment at the Nashville Inn. Everything was now perfect for the young and rising politician.

Then, one night in April, Eliza walked out. When the news got out that she had gone home to her parents, Nashville was excited as it had never been before. Not only was Sam the most popular man in town, he was in the midst of his campaign for re-election. This was tasty gossip.

The courthouse square filled quickly with people that night. The story ran wild through the town. Everybody wanted to know what had happened. Why had Eliza left? Rumors spread with amazing speed. Sam's political enemies accused him of driving out his wife with incredible cruelties. Within hours, public opinion flared. Houston was threatened with mob violence.

Sam sat in his room at the inn, the lamp burning, saying nothing. His political advisers rushed to see him. "You must defend yourself," one of them pleaded. "This thing is getting out of hand. Your political life, and maybe more, is at stake right now. Can't you make a statement?"

Sam sat in a heavy chair, looking tired for the first time in his vibrant life. "I can make no statement," he said softly. "If my reputation can't stand the shock of this, let me lose it."

His friends were impatient with him. They begged him to fight back. "There are friends of yours turning from you even tonight," one friend said. "In the street, you are being burned in effigy. There are dirty stories going around. Sam, you must act."

"This is a painful but a private affair," Sam said stubbornly. "The public has no right to interfere in it."

His friends gave up. They were preparing to leave when Sam called them back. "Wait," he said. "This much I must say. I exonerate my wife fully, and I do not justify myself." He stood up and walked to the window. He could see the crowds outside. With his back to his friends, he said, "I am a ruined man, and I will exile myself. I would be grateful if you will take my resignation to the Secretary of State."

The room was quiet. Sam walked to his desk, picked up an envelope, and handed it to them. "Now, will you please leave," he said.

In the morning, Sam walked out of the Nashville Inn. The sheriff and the town doctor, two close friends, carried his bags. As he walked through the streets, small crowds of people followed him, more curious now than angry. Sam walked to the steamboat landing, boarded the packet *Red Rover*, and took himself into exile.

It wasn't until much later, too late to salvage his career or his marriage, that some sense was made of the tragic affair. This woman who had "so strangely changed the face of American history like no other woman by such womanly means" (as a Houston biographer once wrote) had been forced into the marriage by her ambitious parents. She did not love Sam; she may even have considered him a barbarian. And she did love another. Sam, for all his experience with women, knew little about them, and it took him a while to realize what was happening. Then it hit him hard. The loveless marriage brought him heartbreak and humiliation, and there is no way to record the damage it did to his vanity.

It is not an unusual story, but the way it diverted a part of American history made it a vital mystery that has lasted even to this day. Why did Houston resign as governor? Why did he throw away a glorious political career? He could have told his story of a loveless marriage to the people, and they would have listened. He didn't have to throw everything away.

But Sam did throw it away. Why? His pride was incredibly large. His chivalry was thoroughgoing. And in his great heart, he was childlike. He thought it was the only thing to do.

Whether it was or not, he made the magnificent gesture and then walked off into the west. He went back home to the Cherokee nation. The tribe by now had moved again and was on the western slope of the Mississippi River. Oo-loo-te-ka, now sixty-five, was head chief of all the Cherokees. When Sam arrived at Webber's Falls, an Indian trading post, Oo-loo-te-ka was waiting for him. Somehow, the old chief had known he was coming and that he would need help. The chief helped him by asking him to help the Cherokees. The light came back to Sam's eyes. He had something to work for.

He gave up his American citizenship and was made a citizen of the Cherokee nation. He shaved his face, except for his mustache and a goatee, he plaited his hair, draped an Indian blanket around his shoulders, and figured he had turned his back on civilization forever. He was now "The Raven." And he went to work. The Indians were being cheated out of rations; treaties were being broken by the white man. Sam had a plan—getting the Cherokee, Choctaw, Osage, and Creek tribes together into one mighty nation. It was a dream of empire.

Sam visited the other tribes, counciled with them, and learned of all their grievances. Finally, he went to Washington as the official ambassador of the Indians.

Official Washington did not know what to expect when Sam, dressed as an Indian, showed up. How would President Jackson take to him? The answer came quickly. Old Hickory welcomed him warmly and held a reception in his honor.

Afterwards, the two friends met to discuss business. "The Indians aren't getting proper rations," Sam told the President. "I am applying for the contract. The price is now seventeen cents per ration. I will take only twelve cents per ration, and I will feed them better."

Jackson nodded. "I know you will, Sam. I'll see what I can do. This isn't an easy matter. The Indian agents have friends here, and they're not friends of mine."

Old Andy was so right. Within days, a congressman named William Stanbery, a Jackson enemy, made a speech claiming that a contract for the Indian rations had been illegally given to Houston. It wasn't true. When Sam heard about the charge, he wrote the congressman a letter, asking if he had been quoted correctly. Stanbery's answer, given to an emissary, was that Sam Houston, "that exile," was too insignificant to notice. This was a blow to Sam's honor and vanity, a tough combination to attack.

"So he doesn't know me?" Sam said. "Then I'll introduce myself to him."

He made a public announcement that he would thrash Stanbery the first time he saw him. Stanbery armed himself, but Sam refused to carry a pistol. Instead, he toted around a hickory cane he had made for Jackson. He didn't go looking for Stanbery. He preferred letting the gentleman stew.

Then one morning, walking with a senator and a congressman down a Washington street, Houston saw Stanbery. He walked up to him, stood spread-eagled before the man, and asked: "Are you Mr. Stanbery?"

"I am, sir."

"Then you're a damned rascal!" Houston shouted and gave him a whack on the head with the cane.

Stanbery, a good-sized fellow himself, turned to run, but Sam, not satisfied, leaped on his back and threw him to the ground. Stanbery drew his pistol, pressed it against Sam's heart and pulled the trigger. There was a snap and the flash of the flint. But the charge did not explode.

Sam grabbed the pistol away from him, stood up, raised the congressman's feet in the air, and whipped the cane across his rump. He caned Stanbery unmercifully until the man cried.

It was, of course, a national sensation. People just don't go around beating congressmen in the streets of Washington. Jackson's enemies had Sam arrested and brought to trial before the House of Representatives. The trial took over a month. Sam's lawyer, Francis Scott Key, was timid and halting, and Sam conducted his own defense.

At one point, Jackson, worried about the outcome, went to see Houston. "This buckskin coat will never do, Sam," Jackson said. "Don't you have any other clothes?"

"No I don't sir."

"Then buy some."

"I don't have any money."

"Here's money," Jackson said. "Now get some fancy clothes so you'll look like something when you talk."

When the House became tired of the argument, it decided to vote. But first it spent four days debating what the charge should be. It was finally voted, 106-89, that he should receive a reprimand. Then the Speaker of the House, who had gotten drunk with Sam the night before, stood up, rapped his gavel, and delivered a flowing eulogy to the noble gentleman, Sam Houston, ending with: "I do hereby reprimand you."

Later, Sam demanded an investigation of the original charges, and after six more weeks of Congressional study, he was vindicated.

The significant thing about the incident was that Houston still had the luck, daring, and shrewd calculation of a successful politician. It was no accident that he beat up poor Stanbery, or that he used a cane. Houston stated the case himself later: "I was dying out, and had they taken me before a justice of the peace and fined me ten dollars, it would have killed me. But they gave me a national tribunal for a theater, and that set me up again."

Brooding over the way fate had treated him, when he got back to the Cherokee encampment he began drinking excessively. He had always been a sturdy drinker, but now he let it get away from him. Now he became known as Oo-tse-tee Ar-dee-tah-skee—Big Drunk. "He buried his sorrows in the flaming bowl too deeply," the Indians said.

When he rejoined the tribe, Sam met Tiana Rogers, whom he had known as a half-naked ten-year-old at the Hiwasse in Tennessee, where he first lived with the Cherokees. Tiana, of all his Indian girl friends, was the only one who was free now. She had been married, but "divided the blanket." She was a tall slender beauty of thirty and top blood in the tribe. She moved in with Sam in a log house he had built. There was no ceremony, but the Cherokee considered them man and wife. The missionaries did not. It didn't matter. They lived like man and wife. When Sam became Big Drunk, only Tiana stood by him. The other Indians made fun of him, although they always protected him from any harm.

Once, however, in a drunken rage, Sam hit his foster-father. The Indians gave him a violent beating for it. It was Tiana and Oo-loo-te-ka who bathed his wounds and brought him back to life.

Because of some strange code, he refused to drink with Indians. Either he got drunk alone, or in the company of white men at the nearby army encampment, where, because of his once high military rank, he was welcome at officers' mess. Often he would end one of these visits on his face in the dirt and have to be carted home by the Cherokees.

The "tear" ended in September of 1831, when he returned to Tennessee in time to be at the bedside of his dying mother. When he returned to his wigwam, he was sober, and he stayed that way.

There is little doubt that Andrew Jackson definitely had his eyes on Texas for a long time, and that Sam Houston was his advance man. In November, 1832, Sam said goodbye to Tiana, leaving her their home, Wigwam Neosho, his lands, and two slaves, and rode off on a pony without a tail named Jack. He was going to Texas.

On the ride to Red River, Sam had company, an able drinker named Elias Rector. Just before crossing the sprawling river, Sam traded his nag for Rector's handsome horse.

"General," Rector said, "I want to give you something before we separate, but all I have as a gift is a razor."

"I accept your gift," Houston said, "and mark my words. If I have any luck, this razor will some day shave the chin of the President of a Republic." Sam knew why he was going to Texas.

It was wild, open country, populated by emigrant Americans, and the people were stirring. One attempt, a mild one, had already been made to free the territory from Mexico. Sam rode in at the right time. Within a year, Texans had him pegged as their leader. His fame had preceded him, and that was a good start. It was easy for the big fellow to take it from there. "That's Sam Houston," the people would say. "He says there is going to be a war in Texas before long, and he means to figure in it."

Texas was divided at the time, between people who wanted to fight the Mexicans and people who wanted to negotiate peacefully for independence. Sam sided with the cautious faction. He believed that freedom should come by slow steps and not by revolution. For one thing, he didn't think Texas could win a fight against Mexico.

The Mexican dictator, Santa Anna, didn't think so either. But he wanted a war—to distract his people from the scandal, violence, and outright thievery by his government back home. He kept sending troops into Texas on nuisance raids; to confiscate arms, burn a village, or incite the Indians.

Late in 1835, Santa Anna sent a platoon of soldiers into a small village called Gonzales to take a brass cannon away from the Texans. The Americans buried the cannon, and the Mexicans, angered, rushed in one hundred dragoons. They were met by one hundred Texans waiting with a sign that said: "Come and take it." When the Mexicans hesitated, the Texans attacked. The war was suddenly on.

Santa Anna moved troops into the southern tier of the country, pillaging village after village. But the Mexicans were not resolute soldiers. One skirmish and they were ready for a furlough. The enemy was disorganized and uncombative.

A Texas provisional government had been set up, and Sam was named commander of the army. That was a joke— there were altogether thirty thousand Texans. When he tried to mobilize an army, he ran into all sorts of trouble. There was no money; the little government was already riddled with corruption, thieves, and overly-ambitious men; and the only arms they had were knives and rifles. With it all, Houston was to fight an enemy of seven million people who had an established army and navy, and an arsenal.

Quickly, Sam made long-range plans for the conduct of the war. He put together whatever army he could and began falling back, avoiding direct battle. Delay would give him time to gather men and arms, and retreat would stretch out the Mexican brigades.

The task was more difficult than even Sam had anticipated. When he avoided battle, the people screamed. When, after a few months, he sent men into San Antonio on a sneak attack and routed the Mexican garrison stationed there, the people said the war was over. Houston said it was just beginning. Attempts were made to remove him as commander-in-chief; other officers took off on assaults of their own. Everybody wanted to be a hero, and nobody was taking orders. It was a mess.

One day, after several soldiers had deserted and returned to their farms, Sam climbed on his horse and rode away from his headquarters. He rode for almost half a day, then suddenly stopped alongside a spring. He watered his horse, washed himself, and lay down in the shade of a tree. As he looked up at the blue sky, there was a mist of tears in his eyes. This, he thought, was not for him. What good are plans and dreams if people won't follow? Hate and division had taken over his little, weak, hungry army—and the army had taken over the government. Would victory be better than defeat? He looked out across the brook and he remembered Tennessee. Why not give it up and go back to the Cherokee? For hours, he brooded and rubbed his hands and muttered, "Damn, damn, damn!"

Finally he made up his mind. "I'll fight and I'll win," he said out loud and rode back to his camp. He arrived there just before the news came of the Alamo.

Santa Anna had been marching, as Sam thought he would, with a large army made up of Indians, convicts, and anyone else he could frighten into fighting. Altogether, he had seven thousand men, and he was determined to pillage the land, settlement by settlement. The defeat at San Antonio had infuriated him, and that was where he went first.

Only 182 Americans were at the San Antonio garrison when Santa Anna marched in. They knew what he had planned—he had already massacred villages below the town—and they knew that behind San Antonio there were many other settlements that did not know that Santa Anna was on a rampage. So they had to stop him here, at least long enough to give the rest of Texas time to prepare to defend itself. They could not expect to fight him in the streets of San Antonio, so the Americans fell back to the Alamo, an old abandoned mission outside of town.

For eleven days, they held him off, but finally they fell. All of the "Texas dogs" were slain, but it had cost Santa Anna four hundred dead, three hundred wounded, and countless deserters.

But Texas did not prepare while Bill Travis, Jim Bowie, Davy Crockett, and the others held the mission. Instead, the country became panicky. Desertions in Houston's army increased. There were less than four hundred men left, and they were ready to mutiny.

One night, Sam caught the smell of the mutiny. The men growled because there was no food and no clothing. His officers had grown surly. He had to move fast.

He took a shovel and went to the center of the encampment and dug all night. When the men arose in the morning, they found two deep graves and a sign posted between them: "Any man who talks of desertion will be shot." And standing next to the sign was Sam, a musket in his hands. The men believed him; the desertions stopped.

Week after week now, the pattern of the war did not alter. The Mexicans were chasing Houston, and Houston kept running. Santa Anna wanted only to win now, and there were two possible ways—catch General Houston or catch the provisional government. He chose Houston because the government was running faster than the army was.

What Sam's plan was no one knew—if he had a plan at all, they growled. He was an inscrutable man; he asked for no advice and he took none. His officers tried to consult with him, but he kept his own counsel. The government, in an effort to find out what he was doing, planted a spy in his army.

Once, when a courier from the government caught up with him and delivered the demand that he explain his actions, Sam answered: "I consult no one; I hold no councils of war. If I err, the blame is mine." That was his way.

But of course he did have a plan. As he backed away from the Mexicans, he kept picking up stragglers, horses, even volunteers. The $70,000 that had been borrowed from the United States was gone, and he needed more arms and ammunition, more food and wagons. This was the only way to get them.

Finally, Sam decided he was ready to fight. He had 750 men, two field pieces, and three wagons. Now he had to pick his spot. He knew that Santa Anna would not pursue him for too long. The man was avaricious; he would ravage the land. Sam was right. Santa Anna stopped at every village he captured and looted it. He crossed the Colorado River, and continued to pillage.

Then one day, the Mexicans received word that the Texas cabinet was lodged in a town nearby. Santa Anna left the bulk of his army to continue scavanging, and with a picked body of men, he made the forty-mile dash to where the government was holing up. "I'll be back in three days," he said to his generals. "Wait for me."

Sam had been keeping in close touch with Santa Anna's doings. He had his scout, Deaf Smith, tracking the Mexican Army. Smith rode into Houston's camp late that afternoon to report Santa Anna's movements.

Suddenly, Sam switched his tactics. He began following Santa Anna. Using a steamboat to move his army, he crossed the Brazos River. Both he and Santa Anna were heading toward Galveston Bay, and there was only one way to get back across the river now—at Lynch's Ferry. Otherwise, the Mexicans would have to turn back, right into Houston and his hungry army. It was a daring gamble, and Sam didn't hesitate to take it.

He pushed his men to great speed, and they responded instinctively. He was the hunter now and his men could feel the power mounting. "Old Sam," they cheered as they struggled through rain and mud, "Old Sam." He was forty-three years old.

In two and a half days, the army marched fifty-two miles. On the third night, Deaf Smith swam the river and came back with two captured Mexican couriers, who revealed that Santa Anna had twelve hundred men, and that the rest of his army was strung out behind him.

Now Sam knew what he had to do. He slammed his huge fist against a pine stock. "We have them," he shouted, and his junior officers stared at him, startled and still ignorant.

Sam had decided to get to Lynch's Ferry before the Mexicans did, and force the battle where he wanted it. The men moved out on that final day, and by afternoon, were on a high wooded bluff overlooking an open prairie. "We stop here," Sam ordered. Smith, who had been moving ahead of the column, came back with the news that the Mexicans were not at the ferry. Sam had won his race. He posted outposts and gave his men a chance to eat. A cache of provisions taken from a captured Mexican flatboat was broken open, and his men had their first salt, flour, and sugar in many weeks. Fires were set, cattle were slaughtered, bread was made in tin cups, strips of bleeding beef were broiled on bayonets. It was a feast.

Before nightfall, the battlefield was prepared. The two artillery pieces, called the Twin Sisters, were moved into position overlooking the prairie. Camp was pitched in a grove from which the army could begin its assault. After he had secured his camp, Sam went to his tent.

"Check exactly where we are," he told his orderly.

"This is San Jacinto," the orderly told him.

"San Jacinto," Sam muttered to himself, "so this is where Texas takes its stand." He sat down on a log, opened his writing book, and scribbled his final log on what was to be known later as the "Eighth Decisive Battle of the World."

"We prepare to meet Santa Anna," he wrote. "It is the only chance to save Texas . . . We could have had at least four thousand men . . . but we will be only seven hundred . . . but we go to conquest. It is wisdom growing out of necessity to meet and fight the enemy now." Then he slept.

The next morning, Santa Anna came. He had heard that

Houston was ahead of him from some captured settlers. The Mexican didn't know how the American got there, but he figured he must have come the other way. It didn't bother Santa Anna. He could easily demolish such a weak and poorly armed crew. Brazenly, he swung his army into the open prairie and opened fire. When the Americans fired back, he moved out of range and decided to wait for the reinforcements he had sent riders after the night before. He set up camp deep in the prairie, in full view of the Americans, and waited. The *gringos,* he was sure, would not attack him.

And Houston did not attack. His men wanted to make a charge, but Sam refused. He knew Santa Anna. The man lived by fits—he would follow a sudden action (like the brief artillery display) with a lapse into laziness. Delay twenty-four hours and the Mexicans would be less effective.

That night, as his soldiers slept, Sam spoke to his aide: "I know we could have won today, but our loss would have been heavy. Tomorrow, I will conquer, and it will not cost me a dozen of my brave men."

The aide smiled. He believed his general.

Sam stayed up that night until 4:00 A.M. Then he sounded reveille himself, with three taps on the drum, and went to sleep. At nine o'clock, his aide woke him up. "Mexicans," he yelled, "crossing the prairie. They are reserves, sir."

Sam scoffed at the news. "That's not help," he said. "That's just Santa Anna marching his men back and forth trying to feel us. We will not attack. Pass the word." Then he went back to sleep. He knew that these actually were reinforcements, but he didn't want to disturb the aggressive spirit of his men.

At about noon, he woke up again. His officers were standing around his blanket, watching him. "Sir," one of them said, "we'd like to hold a council."

"Certainly," Sam said and got up. "What is it you'd like to council about?"

"Well, sir, we feel there is a decision to be made now, without delay."

"And what is that?"

"Whether to attack or wait for Santa Anna to make the first move, as you seem to be doing, sir."

Sam took a drink from a jug of whiskey. He said nothing.

"I think, sir," a captain spoke up, "that we should attack tonight. The Mexicans, I believe, will not make any advance until tomorrow."

"By your leave, sir," a lieutenant addressed the captain. "I don't think we can afford to wait. Our men are ready now. Delay may be too much of a strain."

And another captain said, "Let's not lose our good position here. Let's wait for them to come to us."

Houston said nothing. He just listened. When a half-hour later, they had talked themselves out, he dismissed them without even suggesting what his thoughts were. Then he called for Deaf Smith. "Destroy the bridge," he told the scout and went to have lunch.

At 3:30 in the afternoon, he ordered his men at parade ready, and by four o'clock, they were prepared. Sam rode in front of them on his beautiful white horse, his flashing sword held around his middle with buckskin thongs.

The single fife and drum played "Come to the Bower I Have Shaded for You," the only song the two fellows knew.

"What about a flag, sir?" a private shouted. "We don't have a flag."

"That's right," Houston said. "We need a flag."

A captain of cavalry stepped forward. "I'll take care of it, sir," he said smartly. He went to one of the wagons and got a wooden shaft. Then he removed a small white glove from his pocket. "My wife's sir," he said as he tied the glove to the shaft. "There, there's a flag." And he held it up high.

"Aye," Houston said, "a flag to do any army proud."

Suddenly there was a—boom! The Mexicans had fired a cannon shot into the woods. Houston dug his spurs into his horse and raced up and down the line. "Hold your fire, men!" he shouted. "Hold your fire!" His men held.

The Mexicans were quiet again. Deaf Smith dashed up. "The bridge at Lynch's Ferry," he mouthed in the funny way of a man who cannot hear what he is saying, "it's down, General. In beautiful flames."

Houston raised his flashing sword, spun it in the air, and stabbed majestically down into the prairie. "All right," he said, "Fight and be damned."

The Texans leaped to the charge. The last army of the Republic was on the move. And for the first time in history, the battle cry, "Remember the Alamo!" was heard.

They raced down into the Mexican camp, and Houston kept ordering, "Hold your fire! Damnit, hold that fire!" The Mexicans, caught in the warm sun of the late afternoon, were not expecting an attack. Sam had been right. Arms were stacked everywhere. Men were washing or napping. Camp followers were cooking in large black stew pots.

Not until his men were in pointblank range did Houston order them to fire, and when they did, Mexicans toppled over like so many crushed sticks. After that first volley, the Americans didn't bother to reload their guns. They were in among the Mexicans now, and turned to hand-to-hand fighting. They used their rifles as clubs, or discarded them for hunting knives. Houston's right leg was hit above the ankle by a stray rifle shot. Then his horse was hit. But the general, standing on his one good leg, fought on, slashing his sword powerfully at the Mexicans around him.

The battle, as a battle, lasted just under twenty minutes. The few Mexicans who fought back were quickly slain. Many others, though, dropped to their knees as the Americans ran over them, yelling, "Me no Alamo." Still others ran into the marshes. Santa Anna, who had escaped after the first blast of rifle fire, was caught at the burnt-out bridge and brought back. Others were not so lucky. The cavalry ran down most of the escaping Mexicans and massacred them. The foot soldiers slew all they could reach. It was not until hours later that officers were able to halt the last of the slaughter.

The casualty roll indicated the success of the battle. The Americans had suffered six killed and twenty-four wounded. The Mexicans had 630 dead, 208 wounded, and 730 prisoners of war. The spoils of the battle included 900 English muskets,

300 sabers, 200 pistols, 300 mules, 100 horses, clothing, tents, supplies, the camp followers, and some $12,000 in cash. The money was split among the officers and men; the average take was about $7.50. It was the first money they had received in the entire campaign.

The war was actually over, but no one realized it yet. The great victory at San Jacinto brought swarms of volunteers to the army. There was an abundance of arms and equipment. But with Santa Anna a prisoner of war, Mexico did not feel like fighting. There was no formal declaration of peace, or even a notification that the Mexicans had had it. They simply stopped fighting and went home.

Houston, his wound serious, resigned as commander-in-chief, and went to New Orleans for medical treatment. But while he was a hero to most Texans, he was still a feared and resented enemy to the provisional government of petty thieves and crooked politicians who had taken over. A small Texas war vessel, belonging to the Republic, was sailing from Galveston to New Orleans, and Houston asked for passage. But the government refused him. He had no money, since he had received no pay for his military services, and he had to make a deal with the captain of an American schooner to take him, promising that he would pay later. And the hero of Texas, a bankrupt and a wounded man, sailed away from the republic he had just made free.

Only this time Sam wasn't leaving as an exile. He knew he would be back. Meanwhile, New Orleans gave him the welcome Texas had failed to. And the doctors were able to save him, even though gangrene had set in. As Sam convalesced, the news from Texas became worse instead of better. The bitter wrangling for power was going full blast. The cabinet was being changed every day. Petty bickering ruled the nation. Santa Anna's capture had stopped the war without ending it, and now the government wanted to execute him. This, Sam was sure, would mean a new war and a bad policy for a new country. What did those jackals think would happen to Texas prisoners still held in Mexico, Sam thought, if they executed the head of the country? Santa Anna as a live prisoner was Texas' best ally at the moment.

There were other problems. The Indians were acting up, the government couldn't collect taxes, and the army, now at twenty-five hundred, wanted to take over. A general election was called, but no one knew how to carry it out because the constitution had been lost. Finally, rules of order were prepared, candidates were announced, and Texas' first election campaign began. But there was no word from Houston. People expected him to come home and take over, but Sam stayed away. He was waiting for a firm call to return; he wanted to be drafted. The date of the election was September 5, 1836, and two weeks prior to it, spontaneous meetings all over Texas submitted Sam's name as a candidate for the office of president. On August 25, eleven days before the election, Sam agreed to run. He was quite a politician. He received 5,199 votes to his combined opposition's 1,330.

President Houston had a remarkable administration in the wild country. He couldn't collect taxes, he couldn't get a bond issued, he couldn't borrow money from the United States, and his enemies worked overtime to sabotage his regime. Still, he got things done; things like some schools and a few roads and an element of justice. Before, justice in Texas had meant a lynch mob, working fast and with finality. Houston, a practical man of principle, made his adjustments fit the times. He sent out a fellow called Three-Legged Willie, because he had substituted a pegleg for a useless one, which he had strapped up behind. The people didn't want Houston's justice, but Willie gave it to them anyway. Once he asked a lawyer what his authority was for a particular point of law, and the lawyer drew a Bowie knife, laid it on the table, and said, "There is the law."

Three-Legged Willie drew a pistol, laid it on his desk, and replied: "And there is the constitution, and the constitution takes precedence over the law." Justice was done.

Houston was a man of imagination, and he used it well in those days. At one point in his administration, army commanders decided that their military might should march on the capitol (now in the town of Houston), chastise the president, throw out the Congress, and "give law to Texas." They were feeling their muscles, and they wanted to invade Mexico.

Sam drew them to the capitol by deftly letting the word circulate that maybe he was in the mood to support their invasion, and now was a good time to see him. The army men came to Houston, of course, and when Sam learned that they had arrived, he swiftly sent secret orders giving the entire army thirty-day furloughs, with paid transportation to the United States. By the time the army commanders got back to their stations, their troops were gone. There was no more army, and there was no march on the capitol.

In 1838, Sam stepped down and called for a new election. By law, a president could not succeed himself. The new president, Mirabeau Lamar, had been a member of the opposition to Houston, and he decided not to invite the "Father of His Country" to his inauguration. This didn't stop Sam. He attended the ceremony dressed up like George Washington, and when the crowd spotted him, it went wild. The people insisted he make a speech, and Sam unshrinkingly walked to the porch of the capitol and spoke for three hours.

He was not yet forty-six years old, but after giving up the reins of government, Sam went into what for him would have to be called retirement. He got elected to the House of Representatives for an east Texas district, he ran a stock farm, and he got married. (Apparently, but not definitely, he had divorced Eliza by now.) On a trip to Alabama, he met Margaret Lea, a tall fair girl with violet eyes and golden brown hair, and they were married. She was twenty years old at the time. Under her gentle influence, Sam cut down on his drinking and his cursing. They were, for the next twenty-five years, a very happy couple.

Lamar's administration of the Republic was disastrous. The government was bankrupt; Texas money dropped to twenty cents on the dollar; Congress was ready to dissolve. It was a dismal day, and one of Lamar's grandiose plans had failed miserably, when members of the House, willing to let the government fall, rushed for the doors. But Sam rose and addressed the Speaker. The rush stopped. "Let's hear Old Sam," people cried. The congressmen returned to their seats. And Sam talked, rambling on about how the brave men fought and died for the Republic, not really saying very much, but talking softly, as if soothing a cranky baby. Then, after a half-hour, he said, "Now I move that the House adjourn until tomorrow at the usual hour." Not a member voted against it, and the government did not fall. At election time, the next year, Sam ran for president again. It was the demand of the people, he said, and he won neatly.

Taking over from Lamar was like accepting a receivership. Texas owed $12,000,000 in gold. Its paper money was circulating at three cents on the dollar. There wasn't even enough money in the Treasury to buy firewood for the executive mansion. And the Mexicans had begun nuisance raids. Houston knew Texas could not carry on a war, and his tactics to avoid a battle were simple enough—he worked for peace at the moment and an invasion of Mexico later, not by Texas but by the U.S. He still knew how to wait for his chance.

He battled down those Texans who wanted to invade Mexico now. He badgered the British and French into treaties; he bluffed the Mexicans with marches of large armies of unarmed men toward the border. And he got the United States to annex Texas as a state. This is what his young and broken country needed, union with the United States. It happened in 1845, just after Sam had retired from his second term as president, and it meant that the United States took over more land than it already had.

Now there was a new job for Sam. He was fifty-three when he went to Washington as the first United States Senator from the sovereign state of Texas. Wearing a vest of tiger skin and a broad-brimmed hat, and draped in a blanket, he struck Washington as a "magnificent barbarian," somewhat tempered by civilization. He was as dramatic as ever, and his work was passionate and brilliant. Immediately and instinctively, he dedicated himself to the cause of union. As a Southerner from what was now a border state, he fought the

South on the issues of slavery and secession. The fight began in 1848 and continued right up to the Civil War. When he would rise on the Senate floor to speak against slavery as a moral wrong—he recognized it as a practical expedient—he was hooted by Southern senators as a renegade. When he talked against secession, he was attacked as a traitor. During his second term in the Senate, marked by the campaign for Southern confederation by old John Calhoun, Sam stood alone in his fight. He was not with the North because he believed they were a faction too, and they were helping to drive the wedge of disunion. He was for union. After the Dred Scott Decision opened the West to slavery, he knew that he had failed in his one great project—to bring the North and South together, and keep them together. The new President, James Buchanan, was "a Northern man with Southern principles." Disunion was growing, and war, Sam said, was terribly close.

He had wanted to be President, wanted to badly, and he knew that his stand on anti-secession would hurt him. Yet he pursued it relentlessly, until he decided that there was nothing left to pursue. He was tired, and his old wounds were bothering him. He decided to return to Texas in the summer of 1857 to run for governor and stem the tide of popular opinion that was dragging the Lone Star State along with the Southern rebels. He ran an exciting campaign, but for the first time in his career, he lost an election.

Dejected, he went back to the U.S. Senate, from which he had not resigned, and finished out his term. The slavery issue boiled around him, and more out of instinct than optimism, he would rise on the floor and debate the issue against the South and the North. The North was ready to push the South out of the Union; the South was ready to go. And only Sam Houston, it sometimes seemed, wanted to avoid open combat.

After his term, he returned to Texas and ran again for governor.

It was a lonely campaign. Texans were not in a mood to listen to talk about staying in the Union. But there was a saying at the time—"Only two things can draw a crowd in Texas, a circus or 'Old San Jacinto'." Sam drew the crowds, mostly angry mobs looking for a fight. But Sam held them, and then he swung them. The issues were all against him, but he won.

The following year, in the Presidential campaign of 1860, he was sought as a candidate. Northern abolitionists approached him. "You can win," they said. "The North will be for you, and enough of the South."

But Sam had to say no. He wanted to be a national candidate. If he succumbed to running for a faction, any faction, in this fight, it meant the cause of union was completely lost. No, he couldn't become President under any banner that was pushing civil war. He ended up being a man without a party and without a candidate to support. He could back neither Abe Lincoln nor John Breckenridge. Breckenridge was the choice of the secessionists. Lincoln was a Northerner, and would represent only the Northern point of view. Sam loved the South too deeply to support him. But Sam knew that Lincoln would win. In a speech at a Union mass meeting, he said: "The Union is worth more than Mr. Lincoln, and if the fight is to be fought, let us fight it in the Union and for the sake of the Union."

It did him no good; people weren't listening to reasonable moderation. But there was still Texas. "I am making my last effort to save Texas from the yawning gulf of ruin," the governor said. It was a brutal effort. The state was in turmoil. A special convention joined Texas to the Confederacy and demanded that all state officials take an oath of allegiance.

A big public ceremony was held, and as a clerk called the name of each official, the gentleman would walk to the platform amid wild cheers and sign his name to a pledge. When the clerk called, "Sam Houston," there was no answer.

The special convention reconvened immediately, declared the office vacant, and swore in the lieutenant-governor as Sam's successor.

Sam was hurt, and he was mad. A Union agent, posing as a horse trader, came to Austin and arranged a chance meeting with Houston at a hotel saloon. It was easy enough to start a conversation with the governor; nobody else was talking to him. After warming the atmosphere, the agent went to his main task.

"Governor," he said, "I have an offer that can save Texas."

"I doubt if anything can do that," Sam answered.

The agent leaned over his glass of whiskey. "There are fifty thousand troops ready to march into Texas, sir, if you will lead them."

"Young man," Sam said, "in Texas we kill men for such thoughts. I will not sabotage my state, and I suggest you get out before my state sabotages you."

"Sir," the agent continued, "this is no insurrection I'm suggesting. The Union is offering you the rank of major general and the command of an army. It is asking you to defend the United States."

"No," Sam said, now remorseful over what was the obvious arrangement of things. "I cannot even defend Texas, and Texas today is dearer to me than even the United States. I could not desert her."

Sam turned from the agent and walked across the street to his office. The lieutenant-governor was already sitting in his chair. Without a word, Sam gathered his private papers and possessions, wrapped them in a small blanket, and walked out of the office of the governor without a fight. He left Austin (now the state capital) and headed home.

On his way, he stopped in the town of Brenham. There was a raging crowd in the streets, and friends asked him to talk to them, to restrain them from their intent on violence.

"No," Sam said, "that's not my field anymore. They'll just have to stay violent."

He had returned to his horse and wagon, when a group of hotheaded men walked up to him. "We understand you're afraid to make a speech here, Governor," one of them said.

Sam ignored him. He was tired and he didn't want to do what on some other day he would have felt it was his duty to do.

"We dare you, Governor," the man said. "We dare you to try talking to that crowd."

That did it. Sam could not ignore the challenge. Nothing could stop him now. He walked toward the crowd, which had grown uglier. His friends, seeing the dangerous mood, tried to talk him out of it. "It's worse than we thought, sir. You'd better not."

Sam wasn't listening. He walked into the mob, pushed people aside as he made his way, walked to a balcony a few feet above them, and in his deep basso began to talk.

"Put him out," people screamed. "Kill him. The traitor."

One of his friends jumped to the balcony. "We have invited Governor Houston to speak to us," he shouted, holding a Colt revolver in his hand, "and I'll shoot the first man who tries to hurt him. There is no man in Texas who has more right to be heard. And you know it."

Sam began again, and this time the crowd listened. "There's a war coming," he said, "and Texas will be in it. There is no other way. But Texans can handle themselves. They can fight and they can win." The crowd was confused and moved. Sam was the "Father of His Country" again. The arguments and debates were over. Now it was battle and bloodshed, and he was trying to cheer up his people. When he finished, the crowd stood silently as he got into his wagon and rode away.

Sam went home and had his first rest in many years. He and Margaret spent quiet days. Their eight children were grown now. The oldest, Sam, Jr., had joined the Confederate Army and was severely wounded in the Battle of Shiloh. Sam hoped for peace and for the safety of Texas.

In July of 1863, just after the fall of Vicksburg, Sam Houston, age seventy, caught cold and fell into a coma. For several days he lay in his bed, muttering disconnected sounds and gasping for air. Margaret sat with him.

One hot morning, as she held his hand, the great old man mumbled his last words—"Texas . . . Texas . . . Margaret"—and died.

The Saga of Jim Bridger

By JACK PEARL

More words have been written about other frontier heroes, but the measure of this man's worth is in his deeds. Trapping, scouting, or fighting Indians, no one could top the greatest of the Mountain Men

Jim Bridger doesn't rate as much space in American history books as legendary heroes like Davy Crockett, Daniel Boone, or Jim Bowie, whose deeds are still being celebrated on television, in comic books, and on cereal box tops. Unfortunately, Jim was not a very eloquent speaker at a time when a frontier hero had to be his own public relations man. When they weren't killing bear and fighting Indians, Boone and Crockett were busy being their own good-will ambassadors, campaigning for public office, and promoting their own legends. Jim Bridger stayed on the frontier for fifty years and only came back to die.

But if he wasn't a popular figure with all the people, at least among those who knew him—the tough, leathery-faced frontiersmen who pushed the nation's boundaries west, army scouts, guides, boatmen, and trappers—Jim Bridger's stature was supreme. When someone asked Kit Carson, the renowned army scout, what he would do if he ever got lost, he replied with a grin, "Why, I'd yell like hell for Jim Bridger."

Born in Virginia on March 17, 1804, Jim moved with his family in 1812 to St. Louis, where his father opened up a blacksmith shop. Within a few years both his parents died, saddling Jim with the responsibility of supporting his small sister and a maiden aunt. He was only thirteen years old when he took over the heavy duties in his father's smithy, and as a sideline began operating a flatboat ferry on the Mississippi. The St. Louis of that period was pulsating with gaiety, excitement, and color. Working at his forge Jim watched the endless pilgrimage pass his door—immigrant families, riverboatmen, soldiers of fortune, trappers—all seeking fortune and adventure up the broad Mississippi. Many of these travelers stopped at the shop to have a horse reshod, an axe sharpened, or a bent axle hammered out. Everybody seemed to be going somewhere; everybody but Jim Bridger, chained to a rickety shack on the riverbank and a ferryboat that ran in circles back and forth across the river. But of all the adventurers he met, the Mountain Men seemed the most glamorous to Jim; they were a hardy breed who earned their living trapping furs in unexplored ranges of the Rocky Mountains.

The blacksmith shop was a favorite hangout of the Mountain Men. They were lured there by the jug of peach brandy Jim kept in the cupboard for special customers. Lounging around the fire and pulling on the jug, they swapped extravagant tales of Indian fights, barehanded battles with grizzly bears, and other scrapes with death in the wilderness. There were mountain peaks out there, they said, so tall that a man could pretty near see all the way to St. Louis, and at night the stars were as thick as the sparks that leaped from the anvil and so close you could just about reach out and touch them.

By the time he was eighteen, Jim had had all he could take of the blacksmith shop. One morning, while he was waiting for the coals to glow white-hot, he noticed an advertisement on the front page of a newspaper a customer had left in the shop. It called for one hundred young men to sign up with Colonel William Ashley's Fur Company for a three-year expedition into the Rocky Mountains. That same day, Jim sold his business, ferry and all, turned the money over to his aunt, and reported to Major Andrew Henry, Ashley's partner and recruiting officer for the company.

On a crisp spring morning in April, 1822, two enormous keelboats swung out from the St. Louis wharf into the current as the crowds lining the riverbank cheered. The clumsy craft, packed as they were, below and above decks, with the boxes, bales, and equipment of the Ashley Fur Company, wallowed low in the water. The poles of the riverboatmen bent dangerously close to the breaking point as they shoved the big keels into midstream, where a favorable wind ballooned the wide square-sails. Mike Fink, leader of the whole flotilla, tweaked the red champion's feather in the slouch-brim hat that marked him as the King of the Keelboatmen and bellowed, "Set poles for the mountains!" Jim Bridger took a deep breath as a group of men on shore fired a rifle volley in a parting salute and a small cannon boomed flatly across the water. At last they were underway; at last he was going to see those fabulous mountains.

Although the days dragged for most of the Mountain Men, they were filled with magic for Jim Bridger. Mike Fink and his rowdy boatmen were more entertaining than any vaudeville show he had ever seen in a St. Louis theater. And what greater honor could an eighteen-year-old boy wish for than to share a jug around a night-time campfire with men who had traveled with Lewis and Clark and Manuel Lisa.

Then, just below Fort Osage, disaster crippled the expedition. An unexpected eddy swung one of the big keelboats

—the mate to the one Jim was on—broadside to the current, and before they could right her, she heeled over and sank. All hands were saved, but $10,000 worth of supplies and equipment went to the bottom. The accident left half the company stranded without transportation, and it was a long trail on foot from Osage to the Three Forks of the Missouri.

At Great Bend, the riverboatmen had to drag the remaining keelboat around the shallow forty-mile horseshoe. The trappers disembarked with their horses to lighten the load and headed across a neck of land to a rendezvous spot on the opposite side of the bend. En route, a band of marauding Indians stampeded the horses and got away with the entire herd. Without horses, there was no way for the trappers to move their equipment around the Great Falls to Three Forks. "We'll have to fort up at the mouth of the Yellowstone for the winter," Colonel Ashley told the discouraged men.

Before the winter snows set in, Colonel Ashley and a detail of six men headed back for St. Louis to get more horses and supplies. By the time the first blizzard hit Great Falls, the fort was erected and stocked with firewood and supplies. If nothing else, Jim had a preview of mountain weather. For weeks at a time, the men huddled around the roaring fires wrapped in buffalo robes, while the temperature dropped lower and lower and the snow piled up in drifts that finally touched the tips of the pickets. Fresh meat was no problem during the blizzards. Deer, buffalo, and a variety of smaller animals sought shelter in the lee of the stockade and were easy game for the Mountain Men. One day a restless greenhorn, disregarding the warnings of the older hands, decided to hike around the perimeter of the fort. They found his frozen body three days later, not more than one hundred yards from the gate. Jim Bridger swallowed hard. Out of the grim incident came the conviction that was to get him out of many a tight scrape in the years to come: In the mountain wilderness, a man's worst enemy—worse than the Indians, the grizzlies, or the elements—was likely to be himself.

For years, fur trading had followed a set pattern. A

company would build and maintain a permanent post in a rich fur sector; then local Indians would do the actual trapping and bring in the furs to trade for goods. The plan was sound, except for two factors. One, it didn't take very long to clean out the beaver in the local streams; two, the Indians were reluctant to leave their homelands to seek out other streams. The result was that these costly and elaborate trading posts had to be abandoned after one or two seasons at a terrific loss to the company. Ashley and Henry revolutionized the business. The Ashley Company established a number of temporary, inexpensive forts throughout the fur country and garrisoned them with professional hunters. Each summer the trappers from all the posts would rendezvous in a central location for an annual "fur fair." Ashley and Henry would then ship the yearly take back to St. Louis by pack train, paying the Mountain Men off in trade goods, plus a small salary. The company also sold tobacco, whisky, and other luxuries to the trappers, who rarely got to the settlements, at a big profit.

In August, 1823, Major Henry and a party of eighty men, that included Jim Bridger, moved west across the Overland Trail up Grand's River to Fort Henry at the mouth of the Yellowstone River, in what is now the state of Wyoming. All winter Jim had listened to stories about the savage redskins, but to date the only Indians he had encountered had either been friendly ones or plain cowardly horse thieves—certainly not the demons that they had been represented to be in the tales the trappers told. "I ain't even got myself a scalp yet," he grumbled to his friend Hugh Glass, a stocky-graybearded veteran of years of mountain campaigning.

"Yur time'll come, lad, never fear," Glass grinned.

The next day, as they skirted a Ree village near the forks of the Grand River, Jim was treated to his first Indian war cry. It came from all sides at once, a yell that sounded like a chorus of wailing banshees and growling grizzly bears. It took Jim's breath away worse than any blast of wintry air ever had. The hair on his neck prickled as Hugh Glass rose up in the saddle and roared back a grizzly challenge of his

own, "Waaghhh!" He was still not accustomed to this guttural animal cry that the Mountain Men had learned from
the Indians. Since there were no "cuss" words in the red
man's language, he expressed anger, impatience, and frustration by imitating the sounds that the wild beasts made when
they were in a cantankerous mood. There was no oath
stronger than the battle cry of a mad grizzly bear.

"Waaghhh!" Glass roared again as a war party of Rees
came charging out of the woods and surrounded them. Although they were outnumbered, the Mountain Men had the
advantage of being mounted. Crouched low in the saddle,
with arrows and bullets whistling around his head, Jim loaded
and fired his rifle mechanically. Their horses bucking and
plunging, the trappers whirled about him in a wild confusion
of gunfire and screeching. Through the smoke, he saw a
young novice like himself, Walt Riley, pulled from his pony
by two Rees and pinned to the earth with a wooden spear.
Writhing like a worm on a fishhook, Walt was neatly scalped
by one of the Indians. There were more than a dozen Rees
sprawled in the dust too.

Then, as suddenly as it had begun, the battle ended, and
the Indians melted away into the forest again. Jim got off a
parting shot at a retreating brave and had the satisfaction
of seeing him drop at the edge of the clearing.

"Nice shootin', son!" Hugh Glass shouted as he reined up
his horse next to Jim's. There was a thin trickle of blood on
his neck.

"They get you, Hugh?" Jim asked, his voice trembling
with the excitement and nervous tension of his first brush
with the Indians.

"Just a scratch," the old trapper grunted. His eyes crinkled
with amusement. "Well, how about that scalp, boy? That one
you got just now has a prize top-knot." He swung down from
his horse. "C'mon." Jim dismounted and followed him over
to where the dead Indian lay in the high grass. Glass took
his great hunting knife out of its sheath and handed it to
the boy. Jim's face was pale. As he started to kneel, his legs
buckled under him, and he came down hard on his knees.

The knife felt cold and greasy in his wet palm. Motionless, he stared down into the upturned face of the Ree, serene and placid in death. He was a fine-looking fellow. Suddenly Jim looked up at Glass. "Y'know, he's a man just like you and me."

Glass stared at him strangely, "You all right, boy?"

"I just never thought about it before that way."

The trapper was impatient. "Start scalpin', boy. It's no different than skinnin' beaver." Swallowing a clot of vomit that rose in his throat, Jim went to work. It was a messy job. Glass shook his head as he surveyed the tattered strip of flesh that hung from Jim's bloody hands. "You'll do better next time," he said philosophically. "Go over and wipe your hands on them leaves." He took back his knife and stroked the blade clean on his pant leg. Jim turned away and threw up.

When the trappers arrived at Fort Henry, they found that the Rees had gotten there ahead of them and stolen twenty-two horses. In despair, Major Henry had to change his plans once more. Moving up the Yellowstone to the Powder River, they ran into luck at a village of friendly Crows. The Crows had just returned from a successful campaign against the Blackfeet that had netted them over one hundred head of horses. Graciously they traded forty-seven of the horses to their old friend, Major Henry.

Back in the saddle again, Major Henry and his troop moved up to the mouth of the Yellowstone and set up a fort for the autumn hunt. They fanned out and set their traplines in the little tributaries wherever there was a dam, a slide, or other signs of beaver. The hunting was good that fall; even the greenhorns like Jim got more than their share of pelts. It was dangerous work, though. Wading waist-deep in cold mountain-spring water was an unhealthy business at best. Even more dangerous was the peril of Indians and grizzly bear, and more than one unwitting trapper, who relaxed his vigilance as he bent over to check a trap, never straightened up again.

One day Hugh Glass blundered on a female grizzly and her two cubs sunning themselves on the bank of a stream. Before he could bring up his rifle, the mother was on top of him. Hearing his screams, the other trappers rushed to help him, but by the time they had killed the bear, poor Glass looked like a bloody side of slaughtered beef. It was a miracle that he was still alive. They washed and bound his wounds and sat down and waited for him to die. But the feeble spark of life that remained in him refused to go out. After two days, the trappers held a conference. With the winter almost upon them, time was precious. Soon the beaver would be holing up in the mud. Moreover, the country was swarming with hostile Sioux and Rees, and for the past week the party had been under the surveillance of Indian scouts. They had to keep moving if they wanted to stay alive. There was only one answer; they would have to leave Glass behind. Major Henry asked for two volunteers to stay with the wounded man. "It won't be for long," he assured them. "He can't possibly last out the week." No one stepped forward. At last, moved by the thought that his old friend Glass would be left to die alone, Jim Bridger moved out of line. "I'll stay," he said, trying to control the tremor in his voice. Immediately, another man by the name of Fitzgerald joined him. The trappers had difficulty concealing their surprise. Fitzgerald had the reputation of being a little too good at sleight of hand with the cards, and of shirking unpleasant duties. They regarded him with new admiration.

That night, Jim Bridger and Fitzgerald huddled in their blankets beside the inert figure of Hugh Glass, talking in low tones. They didn't dare light a fire. "Listen to that death rattle, Jim," Fitzgerald said. "He's goin' fast." He looked at Jim shrewdly. "We may as well haul out of here right now." Jim was shocked. "We gave our word we'd stay until he was dead. And I aim to keep it." Fitzgerald shrugged and rolled over on his side. In a few moments, he was snoring.

Hugh Glass was still alive the next morning; barely breathing, but still alive. Fitzgerald was getting fidgety. "Don't that damned old fool know when he's dead?" he whined.

His eyes kept nervously searching out the shadows of the forest. Glass had been unconscious for over twelve hours now, the life ebbing slowly out of his body through the blood-stained bandages. That afternoon, Fitzgerald scouted the upper ridges of the ravine they were in. He was back quickly, white-faced and breathless. "I saw two Injuns; Rees, it looked like. They passed so close to where I was hiding I could've touched 'em. They'll get us tonight for sure." As darkness closed in, he kept hammering away at Jim, painting a horrible picture of the tortures that were in store for them if they were captured. "Old Glass, he's the lucky one. They can't hurt him. He's got both feet through the gates of heaven; only thing's holdin' 'em back is his cussed stubbornness."

Finally, Jim couldn't stand it any longer. Glass was barely breathing now, anyway. "All right," he yielded. "Let's go." And so they took Glass's rifle, his powder horn, his knife, and all his possessions and headed off into the night. They caught up with the rest of the trappers at the fort at Yellowstone. After several sneak raids by Blackfoot and Gros Ventre Indians, that cost them two dozen horses, the party decided to move up river. In the Big Horn country they split up into two groups. Jim rode with Etienne Provost, one of Ashley's lieutenants. They headed west over the Continental Divide and up the Green River. The hunting was good. In December, so loaded down with furs that they could hardly carry them, they headed back to the fort on the Big Horn River to rest up for the winter. It was a happy time for most of the Mountain Men; all they had to do was to lounge around and grow fat, like hibernating bears. Many of them took wives from the friendly Assiniboin and Snake tribes and set up housekeeping at the fort. Everyone was contented except Jim Bridger. Time had only aggravated the guilt of his treachery to his old friend Hugh Glass. He couldn't sleep, he couldn't eat, and every time he closed his eyes he could see the still white face of the dying man accusing him out of the darkness.

One bitter cold night in February, Jim returned to the

stockade after an all-day hunt for meat. He left his horse in the corral and was tramping through the snow to his hut when a tall figure stepped out of the shadows of the pickets and barred his way. Jim looked up into a gaunt bearded face, ghostly white in the moonlight—the face of Hugh Glass. Tongue-tied by fright, he was slammed back against the fence by a scrawny but muscular arm. A powerful hand closed on his windpipe. As he felt his breath cut off, he suddenly realized that this was no phantom, but a flesh-and-blood man.

"Hugh Glass!" he gasped.

"Aye," the man snarled. "Now give me one good reason why I shouldn't cut your black heart out, boy."

Amazingly, for the first time since he and Fitzgerald had run out on the dying man, Jim felt at peace. Tears rolled down his cheeks, and, unexpectedly, he began to laugh. Dropping to his knees, he hugged Hugh Glass's legs, babbling like a crazy man. Glass listened in fascination as Jim blurted out how they had left him to die and told of the awful remorse he had been suffering. "Hit me, kick me, cut out my heart! I don't care what! You're alive, Hugh Glass, and that's all that matters!"

The old trapper shoved his knife back in its sheath. "Get up, boy," he growled. "Let's talk about it over the fire."

That Hugh Glass recovered from his wounds is amazing in itself. But that in his pitiable, weakened state he was able to survive in the mountain wilderness, without horse, rifle, or even a knife, and eventually fight his way—creeping and crawling at first—hundreds of miles back to civilization is one of the most fantastic stories in frontier history. As he told it in detail to the trappers around the fire, the men heard him in silent wonder, mugs of liquor sitting untouched in their laps. When he had finished, Glass puffed on his pipe and peered solemnly through the smoke at Jim Bridger, who was trying to make himself as inconspicuous as possible. "I ain't mad at Jim, really," he said. "I just wanted to throw a scare into him. The truth is, iffen he and Fitz hadn't left me, I think I would have died for certain. But when I came to and found that they had skipped out and took all my gear to boot, I was just too mad to die. I made up my mind I was going to carve my initials in their gizzards if it was the last thing I ever did." The tension broken, the trappers joined in with a hearty laugh.

Still ashamed but happy, Jim made a resolution. A man had to listen to his heart even if it meant losing his head. "Only Jim Bridger knows what's right for Jim Bridger," he told himself, and for the first time in months he felt like a whole man.

Jim Bridger learned his trade well. In 1824, his catch of beaver surpassed that of any other trapper in the outfit. But what most impressed the other Mountain Men was Jim's phenomenal memory. Once he had explored a section of country, he never forgot it. Weeks or months later, he could sit down and scratch out a map on the back of a hide in berry ink, filling in all the details down to the last hummock, stream, rock formation, and dead tree. Jim had the passionate love for nature that makes a true explorer. When he wasn't packing mules, breaking horses, hunting, or trapping, he would head into the unknown just for the thrill of seeing for the first time a snow-capped mountain peak or discovering a lake, flashing like quicksilver, in a green valley. He would sit for hours on the desolate prairie and watch the wind come rolling over the tops of the grass, like waves across the sea.

In the fall of 1823, Jim and his friend, Tom Fitzpatrick, discovered South Pass, a narrow defile slicing through the Continental Divide. South Pass opened up the rich fur country of the far Northwest to the fur trappers, and it provided an easy route for the thousands of settlers who later flocked to Oregon and California.

To settle an argument with another trapper on the course of the Bear River, Jim built himself a "bullboat," and successfully navigated the river's treacherous canyon rapids. Once he had proved his theory about the Bear, Jim decided to have a look around this strange country. From the top of a hill, he spotted another small river about two miles away that ran to the west. Lugging his light bullboat overland, he set out to find out where the unfamiliar stream led. After winding about thirty miles through reed marshes, it emptied into a sprawling body of water that stretched westward as far as the eye could see. Noticing that his boat seemed more buoyant than before, Jim trailed a hand over the side and tasted the water. The strong bite of salt pinched his mouth. When he reported his discovery to the men back at camp, they were convinced he had found the Pacific Ocean. But Jim's grasp of the topography of the northwest quadrant of the continent ruled that possibility out.

"Nosiree." He shook his head. "That's a lake; maybe the biggest damned lake in the world."

Great Salt Lake in Utah was Jim Bridger's pet discovery. He became extremely possessive about the whole Salt Lake Valley, and on his own charts he listed it as "Bridger's Hole."

It was along about this time that Jim became ambitious. He had learned all there was to learn about the fur trade, and he was getting tired of living from season to season as Colonel Ashley's hired hand. In 1826 Ashley sold out the company to Smith, Jackson, and William Sublette, three of his chief lieutenants, and retired a rich man. Jim wasn't envious, but he was practical enough to realize that his only future lay in becoming a boss man, or as the trappers termed it, a *booshway* (from the French *bourgeois*). In 1830, the new triumvirate in power decided to take their share out of the company, return to civilization, and enjoy their profits. This was the chance Jim had been waiting for. He and three close friends who shared his views pooled their resources and acquired title to the company. Under the new ownership of Milton Sublette, Henry Fraeb, John Gerais, and Jim Bridger, it became known as the Rocky Mountain Fur Company. Each of the new owners became the captain of a brigade of trappers, each of the brigades covered an appointed territory. The Rocky Mountain Fur Company was one of the best organized outfits in the Northwest.

Bridger and his partners soon learned that the rewards of managing a business frequently were balanced by plenty of headaches. In two years, the Rocky Mountain Fur Company collected about $80,000 for its furs. Against this, it cost the firm $60,000 to buy and transport trade goods from St. Louis to the summer rendezvous and pack the furs back to civilization. Because they lacked the capital to pack in their own goods, as Ashley and Henry had done, they had signed a contract with Bill Sublette, one of the former owners, to be their middleman. Like a great many middlemen, Sublette ended up with a lion's share of the profits. He also received $8,000 commission for marketing the furs back in St. Louis. So, in two years, the five partners split up only $12,000 among them, and out of that they had to pay wages to their employees. Not the least of their troubles was the increasing competition in the 1830's from other companies, like American Fur and Hudson's Bay, and numerous "free" trappers working independently of the major outfits. Beavers were plentiful, but the men had to work harder and longer to get them. The Rocky Mountain Fur Company had by far the greatest reputation in the field, and the best is always imitated. Rival trappers would follow Bridger's men when they set a trapline and place their traps in the same streams.

In the spring of 1831, Bridger and his partners, disgusted with the tactics of their competitors, moved their headquarters from the Green River four hundred miles west to Pierre's Hole near the forks of the Snake River. The American Fur Company followed them. In desperation, Jim headed west into the forbidden Blackfoot country. On October 4 of that year, Vanderburg and Drippe, two scouts for the American Fur Company, were ambushed and killed by Indians. The rest of the expedition turned tail and headed back for more civilized regions.

The elation of Bridger and his party on shaking their competitors was short-lived. As they were crossing the rise of a hill, they came face to face with a big Indian war party on an adjoining hill. Jim and Tom Fitzpatrick, riding at the head of the column, reined in their horses and gave the signal to halt. "Now we're in for it," Fitzpatrick said.

"Blackfeet." Jim's eyes swept along the line of Indians. "At least two hundred of 'em. And all painted up for trouble." He looked back across his shoulder. Like well-trained soldiers, the trappers were fanning out across the ridge. The Indians were scattering across the face of the opposite hill, taking advantage of the natural defenses of the rocky terrain. Turning to his men, Jim said: "We ain't gonna look for trouble. Don't fire unless they rush us." Digging his heels into his horse, he rode part way down the hill with his hand raised, palm to the Indians, in a gesture of peace. The Blackfeet held a quick council of war around an elaborately dressed and painted warrior who was obviously the chieftain. A little later the chief detached himself from the group and rode down the hill, holding a peace pipe high in the air, A retinue of eight warriors followed a few paces behind him. Jim signaled to the Mountain Men and prodded his own horse forward. Fitzpatrick and six others fell in behind him.

The two parties met on the flat sandy floor of the valley between the two hills. Jim reined up a few feet from the Blackfoot chief and extended his right hand. The chief took it solemnly. Then both parties dismounted. Jim Bridger took a saddle blanket and folded it on the ground before he sat down. It was a habit that led the Northwest Indians to refer to him as "The Blanket Chief." The Indian chieftain's eyes widened. In the prairie dialect of the Blackfeet he said, "Chief Sun has heard much talk of 'The Blanket Chief.' He has always wanted to smoke with him." There was a note of respect in his voice.

Jim acknowledged the honor. "'The Blanket Chief' has heard of the deeds and bravery of Chief Sun," he lied graciously. "He is honored to smoke the pipe with the great chief." After the exchange of some more mutual praise, Jim invited the chief to share his blanket. When they were settled, the rest of the Indians and trappers squatted in a circle around them. The peace pipe made the rounds three or four times, while Jim and Chief Sun exchanged small talk. Finally, the powwow broke up on a friendly note and the two parties mounted their horses again. Chief Sun and Jim were concluding a final pledge of friendship when an unfortunate thing happened. As one of the Mountain Men settled himself in his saddle, he accidentally discharged his cocked rifle. The bullet plowed into the dirt between the feet of Chief Sun's horse and the animal reared in fright.

The mutual distrust of years between the Indians and the Mountain Men was not a thing to be casually dismissed by a puff of the peace pipe. Nerves were edgy and eyes waiting and watching for treachery. One young brave, unable to see what had really happened, thought his chief had been attacked. Even before the echo of the shot had died away, he had four arrows out of his quiver and was winging them out of his bow at the white leader.

"Duck, Jim!" one of the trappers yelled.

Jim swung sidewise in his saddle to present a poor target and crouched low on the horse's neck. Two of the arrows whizzed over his head. The last two buried themselves high in his back. The white-hot fire radiating from the shafts in his back burned the breath out of him. The landscape was rocking and shimmering. Fighting back a desire to vomit, he wiped his hand across his eyes. At that moment, Chief Sun reached out and grabbed for his rifle. Thrown off balance, Jim went tumbling into the dust. Adrenalin pumped into his veins, combating the weakness in his arms and legs. Fighting mad, he bounced to his feet, swinging his rifle like a club. As Chief Sun came charging at him with tomahawk raised for a skull-shattering blow, Jim brought the rifle down hard on the Indian's forearm and had the satisfaction of hearing the bone snap. Bullets and arrows were thick in the air now. Screened by a cloud of dust, the Indians loosed a final volley of arrows and retreated up the hill before the superior firepower of the Mountain Men.

Both sides retreated to their respective hillsides and eyed each other warily for the rest of the afternoon, each fuming over the alleged treachery of the other. When it was dark, they went their separate ways.

While neither of the arrows embedded in Bridger's back had struck a vital spot, the pain was agonizing. With four men holding his arms and legs, and Jim biting on a stick, Tom Fitzpatrick tried to pull them out. Since the arrowheads of the Blackfeet were barbed like fish-hooks, it was no easy matter. He managed to wriggle one loose in a bloody operation, but the other was firmly hooked around a rib. Eventually, the blood-soaked leather thongs which fixed the head to the arrow stretched enough to allow Fitzpatrick to remove the shaft. In spite of the pain, Jim was able to travel.

For three years, Jim carried the stone arrowhead in his back, until a surgeon at Fort Laramie cut it out with a Bowie knife in a table-top operation. Witnesses later described Jim's fortitude during the operation as the greatest display of courage they had ever seen.

During the time the arrowhead had been in his back, cartilage had formed around the stone head, welding it to a rib. While the doctor hacked and chopped, Jim lay quietly on the table pulling at a bottle of whisky and joking with his friends. The time of surgery was estimated as "about two and a half pints!"

The affairs of the Rocky Mountain Fur Company went from bad to worse. In 1833, Jim and his partners sold out to the American Fur Company and went to work for their once-hated rivals as free trappers. They worked the country west of the Big Horn River, crossed the Snake, and had many scrapes with the Indians.

Not that Jim went looking for trouble. If he could side-step a fight, he would. But he never backed away from one either, whether he was facing a red man or a white man. A master of the brutal art of rough-and-tumble, he took on and defeated some of the best tribal champions in the North-west, and the Indians were no mean exponents of wrestling science.

During this period Jim made further discoveries in the northwest part of the continent, among them Yellowstone National Park and "Old Faithful" geyser. He was also the first man to set eyes on "Two Oceans Pass," a narrow gorge

8,150 feet above sea level through the Continental Divide. Flowing south from Canada, over the summit of the Divide, is a stream which divides in the pass, half of it flowing toward the Atlantic Ocean via the Yellowstone River and half flowing to the Pacific by way of the Snake River. Jim named the two branches Atlantic Creek and Pacific Creek. Jim and his trappers also broke ground across the plains for the Oregon Trail, which later became the favorite route of settlers heading for Oregon and Washington.

By 1840 it was apparent that the fur trade was doomed. With changing fashions and times, the demand from the East for beaver pelts had dwindled to practically nothing. The trappers were lost men. Some headed back to civilization and took jobs as riverboatmen. A few enlisted in the Army so they could remain on the frontier. It was hard for a Mountain Man to return to the flatlands. Jim Bridger drifted aimlessly from fort to fort, a restless man without purpose or direction.

One day, he and a friend, Louis Vasquez, were sunning themselves in the courtyard at Fort Laramie when a wagon train arrived from the East, headed for the Oregon Territory. Jim studied the tired, dust-streaked faces of the men and women as they plodded through the gate. The hardships of the trail had drained the life out of their bodies and the hope out of their eyes. The men were bent, the women were scrawny, and the children looked starved. Their livestock was lean and bony. And the worst part of the journey still lay ahead of them—dust storms, prairie blizzards, wild rivers, hostile Indians.

Not a sentimental man by nature, Jim was moved by the plight of these people. "Poor devils," he said to Vasquez. "Won't half of 'em make it West."

"*Si*, Jim," the Mexican nodded. "Their bones will whiten in the sun by the side of the trail." He shrugged. "Hell's full of greenhorns."

Jim's eyes narrowed. "You know, Lou," he said. "If a man was to build a fort somewhere on the trail from here to

Oregon, he'd not only be doing those poor greenhorns a good turn, but he could make himself a fortune."

"How so?" Vasquez wanted to know.

"By the time these wagon trains get across the plains, they'll be in bad shape. They'll need supplies, medicine, repairs on their wagons, God knows what else. There ain't any place now where they can git these things. They all got money, but it ain't gonna do 'em any good if they can't spend it."

"Where would you build a fort like that, Jim?"

"I'll tell you. You remember that rendezvous we had at Black's Fork on the Green River? Plenty of green grass and trees; lots of game and fish. Down in the valley, safe from those prairie winds. It'd look like the Garden of Eden to these poor bastards."

"*Si*, but why so far west?" Vasquez looked puzzled.

"The farther they are from the settlements, the greater their needs are goin' to be. And when they see those mountain ranges that lie ahead of 'em, they ain't gonna quibble about price."

Vasquez's eyes lit up, "Are you serious about this, Jim?"

"'Course I am."

The Mexican held out his hand. "You got a partner."

In 1843, Bridger and Vasquez secured a land grant from the Mexican Government, which owned the Salt Lake country, and built Fort Bridger in the valley of Black's Fork in the foothills of the Uintah Mountains. To travelers straggling in off the desert badlands, it was every bit the haven Jim had predicted it would be. Actually, it was a simple place, just an eight-foot stockade enclosing a corral and a few log cabins with dirt roofs. There was a blacksmith's shop, where horses could be reshod, and a carpenter's shop, where rickety wagons could be repaired. There were fresh milk and vegetables, which grew like weeds in the fertile earth. There were whisky, gunpowder, tobacco, and other necessities and luxuries.

Somehow, once the trading post was open for business, their intention to make the most of their bargaining power was forgotten. More often than not, the facilities of the repair shop were placed at the disposal of the settlers so they could make their own repairs—and if a man was hard up for cash, Jim would throw in the materials free. It was common practice too, for Mrs. Bridger and Mrs. Vasquez to carve up a side of beef or a roast suckling pig for hungry travelers. "We ain't makin' much money," Jim commented to Vasquez once, "but it makes me feel good inside to see them half-dead men who come in here go walking out with a spring in their step, rarin' to get at them mountains and Injuns."

But almost in spite of themselves, Jim and Vasquez made money. In 1843, less than five hundred people passed over the Oregon Trail. A year later, the figure jumped to fifteen hundred. In 1845, three thousand people stopped at Fort Bridger. Business was booming.

The traders also pulled down a good revenue from their ferry stations on the Green River, one of the major obstacles on the trail. When the traffic increased, Jim turned over some of these stations to other Mountain Men, old friends from his trapping days. A trip across the Green River brought $1.50 a head to the ferryman.

The years 1843 through 1853 were the busiest of Jim's life. In addition to supervising his trading post and the ferries, he engaged in a moderate fur trade with the friendly Indians in the neighborhood. Although the demand wasn't what it once had been, now that the big companies had closed down, there was still a fair market to be exploited.

Jim was also frequently called on to guide government surveyors and explorers. His natural sense of orientation and distance amazed these men. His judgment was seldom more than a fraction off the readings of their scientific instruments.

On one occasion when a surveyor had measured the height of two mountain peaks rather hurriedly, Jim shook his head. "You're wrong, son. The first one's the tallest; by at least 150 feet, I'd say." Rechecking his calculations, the surveyor discovered he had made an error; the first peak was the taller of the two—by 160 feet!

Like most Mountain Men, Jim Bridger knew that the only

woman who would put up indefinitely with the rigors of mountain living was an Indian woman. And a white man could pick the best there was to offer; even a princess would be honored to keep the house of a great white hunter and trader, cook his food, tan his hides, and bear his children. Jim's first wife was the daughter of a Flathead chief. She died in 1846, leaving him with two small children. The following year, he took himself another wife, a Ute Indian princess. When his children reached school age, he sent them back to a convent in St. Louis for training. A conventional father, he wanted his offspring to have all the advantages he had never had.

Jim Bridger treated his wife with the same respect he would have shown toward a white woman—not like a chattel and a mistress—and he encouraged the men who worked for him to follow his example. It was a well-known fact that the Indian wives at Fort Bridger enjoyed a status not to be found anywhere else on the frontier.

On the other hand, to be treated with such unaccustomed gallantry was too much for a few of the wives and they became arrogant—notably in the presence of others of their own race. In the case of one of Jim's best friends, Joe Meek, it had tragic results. Joe had married the most attractive Snake squaw any of the Mountain Men had ever seen. She was a doe-eyed, round-hipped, slim-legged girl who liked to show off her dusky charms, and one of her favorite pastimes was teasing the Indian braves who came to trade at the fort. Whenever one of them "took the bait," she would suddenly revert to the outraged white man's wife and have him thrown off the premises. Joe Meek never caught on to the game and would have fought for his life defending her doubtful virtue. But she pulled the little prank once too often. One night, as she and Joe were about to go to bed, the door of their hut burst open. An Indian whom Joe had bounced out of the fort earlier that day strode through the entrance, fitting an arrow to the bow in his hand. Even as Meek went for his gun, he heard the twang of the bowstring. At the same time, the girl leaped up from her pallet and hurled herself in front of him. The arrow caught her in the neck. Before the Indian could fit another arrow to his bow, Joe put a bullet between his eyes. A few minutes later, the girl died in his arms. Those at the Fort, who had always regarded Joe's squaw as a "no-good wench," were full of remorse. A woman had to be pretty special to give her life for her man.

In the summer of 1847, Jim was on his way to Fort Laramie when he met a Mormon caravan struggling westward. He stopped to talk with their leader, Brigham Young, on the Little Sandy River. Jim didn't know anything about the Mormon doctrines, but he felt a great sympathy for these people who had been persecuted and driven out of the United States. "Where you headed for, Mr. Young?" he asked.

"Any place that'll have us," Brigham replied. "We don't require much. Just a crust of bread and the right to worship God as we see fit."

"You could settle in the valley with us," Jim offered. As he went on to enumerate all the advantages of the Great Basin, Brigham's eyes lit up. "I like to think of it as my paradise," Jim added, "but you're welcome to share it."

Brigham Young extended his hand. "We'll be honored to share your paradise, Mr. Bridger. It's the first time anyone ever put out a welcome mat for us."

But it didn't take Brigham Young very long to come to the conclusion that the Great Basin wasn't big enough for both him and Jim Bridger. As far back as 1849, he wrote in his journal, "I believe that old Bridger is death on us." Brigham had always preached a gospel of Spartan thrift and the virtue of privation. Bridger's generosity and lavish hospitality were setting a bad example among the Mormon Saints; he was beginning to appear a bigger man in their eyes than Brigham himself. Particularly galling to Brigham Young was the knowledge that one of the major sources of Fort Bridger's growing revenues was the heavy traffic of Mormons from the East. Located on the doorstep of the Mormon capital, Fort Bridger got first crack at the pocketbooks of the new Saints as they arrived over the Oregon Trail. Brigham wanted this monopoly for Salt Lake City to fatten up his own de-pleted treasury.

There was also the matter of Indian trade. The Mormons repeatedly made overtures of friendship to the many Indian tribes in the basin in the hopes of winning their business away from Fort Bridger. But in spite of all the inducements Brigham offered, the red men remained loyal to their old friend, "The Blanket Chief." What was worse, Bridger's arming of the Snake Indians with modern rifles had spiked Brigham's scheme to establish a military dictatorship over the red men.

When the Utah Territory came under United States juris-diction after the Mexican War, Brigham Young was appointed governor of the territory as well as the acting Indian agent. It would appear that the official conscience of the country wanted to make amends to the Mormons for the harsh treat-ment they had been subjected to in the States. In his most fervent prayers, Brigham could not have asked for anything more. This was the wedge he needed to ease Bridger out of the valley.

Brigham's first move as governor was to push a bill through the Utah legislature in 1853, giving a Utah firm a charter to take over the ferries on the Green River. But when the new owners tried to dispossess the Mountain Men, they were driven off at gun point. Unwilling to involve himself in an unpopular war—Jim Bridger was still held in high favor by many Mormons—Brigham Young made no further effort to enforce the new charter for the time being.

In 1856, Jim learned through the grapevine that the In-dians in the valley were mobilizing to attack Salt Lake City. He made a special trip to the Mormon capital to warn Brig-ham of the danger. Distorting the whole purpose of the visit, Brigham accused Jim of threatening to incite the Indians against the Mormons over the incident at the Green River ferries and of selling powder and lead to them as further encouragement of this purpose. As a matter of fact, Bridger had been selling firearms and ammunition to the Indians long before the Mormons arrived in the valley. He was still doing so, as were all the other traders, including the Mormons.

Shortly after the incident, a posse of 150 men converged on Fort Bridger with a warrant for Jim's arrest. Alerted to their approach by "bush telephone," Jim and his family escaped into the woods. When the posse found that the pigeon had flown, they looted the fort, burned all the buildings, and confiscated the property. Later, Brigham Young claimed that he had purchased Fort Bridger from Jim for $8,000 and that the Mormons had merely been clearing their own property.

In November, Jim came out of his hideout in the mountains and hired a government surveyor to survey the thirty-eight hundred acres in Bridger's Valley. The same year, he filed a claim with the General Land Office in Washington. He estimated his losses in the Mormon raid at $100,000.

Discouraged at being driven out of his paradise in the Great Basin, Jim took his family back to Missouri and settled them on a farm. But he was too restless himself to spend much time in civilized country. In 1854, he showed up at Fort Laramie, offering his services as a guide to surveyors, the Army, sightseers, and whoever else was interested in going into the great Northwest.

Meanwhile, relations were becoming strained between Washington, D. C., and Salt Lake City. By the very nature of their beliefs, the Mormons were obliged to recognize only their ecclesiastical leaders. The real power was vested in the Mormon Church, and United States officials assigned to the territory were barely tolerated and completely without power or dignity. The situation finally became so intolerable to the U. S. government that, in 1857, Congress sent an army under General Albert Sidney Johnson to Utah to restore order. It was poetic justice that Jim Bridger was employed to guide the expedition. They camped at the old site of Fort Bridger, which Jim leased to the United States for $600 a year as a site for a permanent army post.

The Mormon War was a short one. Recognizing the hopelessness of his cause, Brigham Young finally knuckled under, and a new government, with officials appointed by the President, was installed in Utah. It was a proud moment for Major Jim Bridger when he rode through the streets of Salt Lake City at the head of a column of United States troops.

With his moderate savings and the income derived from the government lease on his Utah property, Jim could have retired comfortably to his Missouri farm, but something held him back. He had spent forty of his fifty-four years on the frontier. He knew the Indian country better than the Indians did. He spoke more than twelve Indian languages. He could read the tracks of any creature in the woods, two-legged or four-legged, and he could follow a trail, no matter how tangled, through sand or grass or over rock. He could describe a landmark in photographic detail years after he had seen it. A man had a responsibility to use his talents where they would do some good, not to idle them away. Jim decided he would stay in the mountains as long as his country needed him.

In 1859, he guided Captain W. F. Reynolds of the U. S. Army Corps of Engineers in exploring and charting the Yellowstone River and its tributaries. The map which Reynolds made of the region from details supplied by Jim Bridger became the "army Bible" in the big Indian campaigns of later years. In his reports, Reynolds heaped such praise on Bridger that the government employed him on a permanent basis as an army scout at a salary of five dollars a day.

Jim served his last hitch as an army scout under Colonel Carrington at Fort Phil Kearney. When the Civil War ended, the government made drastic cuts in the War Department budget, badly crippling the frontier outposts. Undermanned and inadequately equipped forts constituted a virtual invitation to the hostile tribes to start trouble. The corps of army guides and scouts was hit particularly hard by the economy wave. But when Colonel Carrington received an order to discharge Jim Bridger, who had been assigned to his command early in November of 1868, he refused to comply with it. At this time, Jim was receiving the unprecedented military salary of ten dollars a day.

In spite of the drastic reduction in its army personnel, the government was determined to keep open the roads that led through Indian territory to the western gold fields—in the interests of liquidating the national debt. Carrington, with only a skeleton command, was given the unenviable task of establishing and occupying military posts in Sioux territory in the face of "ironclad" treaties with the Indians that prohibited just such a thing. His orders were to negotiate peacefully for permission to establish these posts—after he had established them.

Repercussions were not long in coming. All along the Northwestern frontier, the tempo of Indian raids on army posts, isolated ranches and settlements, and wagon and pack trains increased. More than one thousand head of horses and mules were captured and over two hundred white men were killed on the Bozeman Trail alone.

With things getting hotter and hotter, Jim set out in July to chart a road which would link up the three new forts under construction in Indian territory—Fort Phil Kearney, Fort Reno, and Fort C. F. Smith—with Virginia City. When he returned to Fort Kearney in late October, a showdown was imminent. The hills around the fort were alive with hostiles; not a day went by without a wagon train being attacked. Miners and settlers camped under the walls of the fort were the victims of sneak raids. The guards around the corral were doubled, tripled, and quadrupled; yet the Indians continued to make nightly sorties on the livestock, making off with a few head of horses or cattle and occasionally a guard's scalp. There was feverish activity to complete the fort before winter set in. Ninety wagons guarded by one hundred cavalrymen made daily trips to cut timber at the Pinery seven miles away, and every day the caravan had minor skirmishes with the Indians.

On October 31, Fort Phil Kearney was completed. It was a gala occasion. A big garrison flag was run up on the proud new flagpole, and the entire command turned out on the parade ground in new uniforms for the ceremonies. On the sidelines, wives and children sang hymns as the band outdid itself. The menial work was finished, and officers and men were eager to get into action. All were contemptuous of the Sioux, and the general attitude was summed up by one captain who bragged that "with eighty men he could whip the whole Sioux nation." Jim Bridger groaned at the bravado of these young greenhorns. "I seen your boys in blue fight down South," he warned Carrington. "All they got is nerve."

The soldiers were rookies for the most part, unfamiliar with the terrain and the tactics and strategy of the battle-seasoned Sioux. Few of them had been in the saddle for more than a few months, and, furthermore, their Eastern-bred horses were unfit for this rocky country. They had cumbersome single-shot rifles, and ammunition was scarce. Jim doubted seriously that any of them could hit an Indian perched on a fence, much less on horseback. And to further point up the unfitness of the garrison, the Sioux and Cheyennes were the best light cavalry in the world and outnumbered them ten to one.

War was an old business to Jim. Valor was one thing, but courage without judgment was suicidal. Storybook heroics had little resemblance to real soldiering, he knew. He did his best to make them understand what "Injun warfare" was all about, but while they listened respectfully to what he had to say, they exchanged sly winks behind his back.

Lieutenant Colonel Bill Fetterman would grin at his crony Captain Fred Brown. "Old Jim must have been some punkins in his day, but he's a regular old lady now."

"Yeah," Brown said. "Why, he's plumb scared to leave this fort. Spends his whole day sitting in that lookout tower looking for Injuns in the hills."

The two young men liked to strut back and forth for the benefit of the ladies, making brash threats about what they would do to the Sioux if they ever got the chance.

Fortunately, Jim Bridger had the solid backing of the commanding officer. At his suggestion, Carrington sent out the wood trains in parallel columns, so that they could set up a corral quickly in case of attack. Lookouts were stationed on Pilot Hill, a strategic high spot overlooking the hilly country surrounding the fort. By means of signal flags they could wigwag information to the fort about Indian troop movements.

On the morning of December 21, the wood train moved out of Fort Phil Kearney on its last trip to the Pinery. One more load of cordwood would fix their fuel supply for the winter. Just before noon, a group of children playing on the parade grounds began to scream, "Indians! Indians!"

Jim came charging out of his hut in time to see the flags wigwagging on Pilot Hill. One of the pickets was riding his horse in a circle, the prearranged signal that meant, "Many Indians are attacking the wood train!" It was a daily routine, and no one was too excited. As was the custom, Colonel Carrington ordered a detail out to relieve the train. At once young Fetterman cornered the colonel and requested permission to command the detail which numbered seventy-eight officers and men—cavalry and infantry—and two civilians.

Since Fetterman was the senior officer under him, Carrington could not very well refuse the request. Aware, however, of Fetterman's recklessness, he gave him strict orders: "Support the wood train; relieve it and report to me. Under no circumstances will you engage the Indians or pursue them over the Lodge Trail Ridge."

Jim watched the column thunder out of the main gate, with Lieutenant Colonel Fetterman and Captain Brown riding at the head of it. Just at that moment, the picket on Pilot Hill flashed an "all clear." The wood train had broken corral and was resuming its journey to the Pinery. The attack was over.

Fetterman brought his men to a halt and studied the wigwagging signal flags. A look of irritation crossed his face. Then he turned to Captain Brown and whispered to him. The captain nodded his head vigorously. Fetterman gave the command to move out, leading his column not to the west road that led to the Pinery, but to the northwest and Lodge Trail Ridge! Jim Bridger cursed softly under his breath as he watched their horses go crashing through the thin ice of the Big Piney River.

For the next hour, Jim and Carrington stood in the lookout tower, the bitter northwind stinging their grim faces. Across the Big Piney the hills were silent. Suddenly a shot rang out, muffled in the distance, followed by the staccato of a volley.

"Looks like Fetterman made contact. I'd say at the Lodge Ridge Trail," Jim said. The sound of intermittent firing was growing fainter and fainter. He shook his head. "They're drawing him across the trail."

Carrington whirled and started down the ladder. "There's a slim chance another detail might be able to get to Fetterman before it's too late."

Within fifteen minutes, two hundred men under Captain Ten Eyck were heading up the Virginia City road. The strategy was to hit the Indians on the flank from the high ground north of Lodge Trail Ridge and take the pressure off Fetterman. Only about one hundred soldiers were left to hold the fort. Carrington ordered all prisoners to be released from the guardhouse and put them on sentry duty on the ramparts. The ammunition reserves were broken out and issued.

Night came, and with it the snow that Jim had been predicting for a week. Still on duty in the tower, he pulled his hat low to shield his face from the wind-whipped crystals of ice. Frequently his eyes would wander to the little clusters of women huddled together on the ramparts, shivering as much from dread as from the cold. Their husbands were out there in the darkness, and it was a certainty that some of them wouldn't be coming back.

It was close to midnight when Jim heard the horses' hooves splinter the ice on the Big Piney; he whirled and went slipping and sliding down the ice-encrusted ladder.

In the shadowy light of the torches, Captain Ten Eyck's face told the story even before he spoke. Jim wasn't surprised when the wagons rolled in through the gate, piled high with the dead. Fetterman's whole command had been wiped out.

The next morning, Jim Bridger led a party of eighty men to recover the rest of the bodies from "Massacre Hill," as it was to be known from that time on. As they rode over the

Virginia City road, Jim reconstructed the events of Fetterman's ill-fated march. The road followed a narrow ridge that sloped down on the north side to the flats of Peno Creek. Where it crossed over the hump of the ridge, the ground was littered with arrows.

"Must have been hundreds of 'em hiding on both sides of the road," Jim explained to Carrington. "Soon as the decoys sucked Fetterman in, they hit him from every which way." He led them down the slope a ways to a field of boulders. Scattered among the rocks were the frozen bodies of the cavalrymen. "When they seen they was surrounded, they took cover in these rocks and shooed off the horses." All the bodies had been stripped and hacked to pieces with savage jubilation by the Indians. A line of dead men stretched from the boulders all the way down to the flats of Peno Creek over a mile away.

Behind one large boulder, they found the bodies of Colonel Fetterman and Captain Brown, lying stiffly side by side. Each had a bullet hole in his temple. Jim eyed the scorched powder burns ringing the red-crusted wounds, and shook his head sadly, "All spunk and no gumption, these cocky greenhorns. They'll never learn."

With the Indians set for a full-scale attack on Fort Phil Kearney, nature came to the rescue with a blinding blizzard that isolated them for almost a month, time enough for a messenger to get through to Fort Laramie with a plea for reinforcements.

Jim Bridger at sixty-four had made his last scouting for the Army. He got his discharge in July, 1868, and hung around for a few months at Fort Laramie, soaking up sunshine and reminiscing with old cronies. But when winter swept across the plains and the sub-zero cold began to bite at his old rheumatic bones, he grudgingly conceded that he had "had it."

He lived the last thirteen years of his life on the Missouri farm with his daughter and her family. Surrounded by grandchildren, who listened dreamily to his stories about the good old days, he was fairly content. When he died in 1881, at the age of seventy-seven, his daughter broke the news gently to her children, "Grandpaw's gone to heaven."

Blinking back his tears, the youngest sobbed, "No he ain't either. He's gone to the mountains." The boy was probably right.

John C. Frémont—Pathfinder

By GERALD ASTOR

Hot-blooded pioneer and soldier, he liked to fight arrogant generals as much as wild Indians. He won an empire for the United States, and died broke.

He was born a bastard; he died a major general. In the seventy-seven years between, John Charles Frémont drained the cup of life dry. He opened up the savage lands of the early West—"from the ashes of his campfires sprung cities." He eloped with the beautiful seventeen-year-old daughter of a United States Senator. He led the successful revolt of California against Mexico, and then faced a court-martial for mutiny. He went from pauper to millionaire and back to pauper in less than twenty years. He was the first man to run for President on the Republican ticket. He was officially charged with the collapse of the Union campaign in the Midwest. He died a poor man, dependent upon government charity for his very existence.

John Charles Frémont was the product of a love affair between Charles Frémon, a handsome emigré French teacher, and one of his pupils, Anne Pryor, the young wife of an old, wealthy Virginia stable owner. When Pryor discovered their relationship, Frémon and Anne ran away together and settled in Savannah, where John Charles was born. Eventually, they moved on to Nashville, where a second child was born, and then to Norfolk, Virginia, where, thanks to the death of Pryor, they were able to marry. The legal union was short, however. One more son was born, and then Frémon himself died. The widow took up residence in Charleston, and it was in this lively city that young John Charles began his education.

His strong point was mathematics, a science that was to prove extremely valuable in his future career.

Frémont (he had added a "T" to the name now) entered Charleston College and appeared an easy candidate for graduation with honors, until he began to neglect his studies for a pretty Creole girl and was expelled.

Through an influential family friend, Joel Poinsett, Frémont secured a position teaching mathematics to the naval cadets aboard the sloop of war *Natchez,* which was making a year's cruise to South America. After an uneventful voyage, Frémont returned home and was offered a position as surveyor with the company that was surveying the route of a railroad through the South Carolina wilderness.

Again an impetuous affair of the heart endangered his career, however, as Frémont became engaged to a girl in Greenville, and then jilted her without cause.

In 1836, the government decided to make a military reconnaissance of the Cherokee Indian territory, and Frémont was included in the expedition. The survey party started out in the winter of 1836-37. On the long trek through this wind-blown, icy wilderness, Frémont accumulated a rough knowledge of frontier existence. He learned to live on flour, water, and raw meat; to pack a mule; and to survive the fierce mountain blizzards. He had an opportunity to study the American Indian. Frémont was a guest at several Indian fiestas that broke up in bloody brawls, as liquor-maddened braves carved up one another with knives.

When the Cherokee survey ended, Frémont was twenty-four years old and a promising candidate for a military career. His patron, Poinsett, was now Secretary of War under President Martin Van Buren. Frémont received a commission as a second lieutenant in the Topographical Corps. His first assignment was a glorious one. Joseph Nicolas Nicollet, the distinguished French scientist, agreed to make Frémont his chief assistant in an exploration of the Northwest, an area which had only been lightly, and mostly erroneously, mapped by Lewis and Clark.

From St. Louis, the party traveled on a steamboat up the Mississippi to what is now Mendota, Minnesota. Here they took to the land and headed west. The expedition spent considerable time among the Indians. Sioux warriors accompanied them on deer and elk hunts, and Frémont profited from the experience of living with the tribesmen. He watched them play their traditional game of lacrosse. He learned how to battle a prairie fire by setting a counterfire.

While stopping at Fort Pierre, Nicollet and Frémont were visited by a Sioux chief. The tribal head arrived at the quarters of the explorers with an interpreter and a pretty Indian girl of eighteen. After they had exchanged greetings, the Sioux chief began to speak rapidly. The interpreter turned to Nicollet and said, "The chief has brought this girl, Smiling Maid, to be a squaw for you. She will cook, wash, and be a good woman for you."

Nicollet grunted in embarrassment. "Tell your chief I am most appreciative of his gift," he said. "But I already have a squaw at home, and the Great White Father will not allow me to have two. However, this young man," he turned to his astonished assistant, "has no squaw, and he could use a woman to look after him."

Frémont turned beet-red as the chief, the interpreter, and

Smiling Maid turned to him. "I—I—" he stammered, "I must refuse your most kind offer since I will soon return to Washington, and I would not like to take Smiling Maid far away from her people, where she would be unhappy." Fortunately, the answer satisfied the Sioux and they left. Nicollet howled with laughter as Frémont buried his nose in his maps.

With the coming of winter, the expedition returned to St. Louis. On the spring flood of the Missouri, they headed back into the Northwest and worked their way into the Dakotas. For the first time, Frémont saw the tremendous herds of buffalo which roamed this territory. No man could fail to be impressed at the first sight of these huge, two thousand-pound beasts with shaggy manes and savage little eyes peering out from their forelocks. Frémont was also treated to an exhilarating view of the prairies, the magnificent beauty of the fertile Dakota lands, lush green woods, that stretched hundreds of miles to the Canadian border.

At the conclusion of this adventure, Frémont returned to Washington, D. C., with his beloved teacher, Nicollet. The young lieutenant was now a fully-accomplished explorer, and the praise of Nicollet quickly earned him a reputation in Washington. There was plenty of time for dalliance in the capital, and it took very little time for Frémont to become embroiled in another matter of the heart.

Senator Thomas Hart Benton was a leading figure in the government, a confirmed believer in manifest destiny—the expansion of the United States as far as geographical factors would permit. When Frémont was introduced to Benton, he made an excellent impression with his grasp of the Northwest and his obvious interest in pushing the exploration of the area. The Senator invited him to dinner on several occasions at the Benton residence, and one evening Frémont was invited to attend a concert at a school in Georgetown, where Benton's two oldest daughters, Eliza and Jessie, were boarding.

At his first glimpse of sixteen-year-old Jessie Benton, Frémont lost his heart.

"Lieutenant Frémont is a very promising member of our

Topographical Corps, my dear," Benton introduced the young officer. "He has just returned from the territory west of the Mississippi."

"Perhaps Miss Jessie would be interested in a firsthand account of my adventures with the Indians." Frémont said boldly.

Jessie smiled coquettishly. "Anything that interests my father is most certainly of interest to me, Lieutenant Frémont. Will you escort me into the concert?"

Later that night, Jessie confided to her sister Eliza, "He's the handsomest man I've ever met."

Frémont was even less abashed in announcing his reaction to the meeting. To Nicollet, he reported, "I have fallen in love at first sight. My one thought is how and where I may meet Miss Jessie again."

Evidently, he made the most of the few meetings he was able to arrange, for it was not too long before Father Benton began to show signs of alarm at the ardor of the young couple. "He has no family and no money—nothing but the prospects of slow promotion in the Army," he told Jessie. "He's no proper match for you."

Using his influence with Poinsett, Benton managed to have Frémont sent out to explore the Des Moines River country immediately. But in a concession to his daughter, he promised that if she and Frémont still felt they were in love at the end of a year, he would permit the marriage.

The expedition was a challenge for Frémont, although, under the circumstances, he was not too enthusiastic about leaving Washington. He did his usual competent job in studying the land, covering about two hundred miles in less than six months, and impatiently hurried back to the capital in September.

A month later, the impetuous pair decided not to wait until the year was out. With the aid of friends, they eloped and were married. The newlyweds kept their nuptials secret for almost a month; then they decided to face the Senator.

As their carriage drew up before the Benton house, Jessie turned to her husband. "No matter what happens, we *are* married and I love you. I'll never leave you." They kissed tenderly while the coachman drowsed in the warm autumn air.

"Frankly, I'd almost rather face a Sioux war party than your father," Frémont said as he helped his wife down.

An aged Negro servant let them in and informed the couple that Senator Benton was reading in his library.

When the pair entered the room, the Senator looked up. "Well?" he asked suspiciously. "What is it?"

"Senator Benton," Frémont began, "several months ago, Jessie and I agreed to wait one year before being married."

"If you are going to ask me to release you from that pledge," the Senator warned, "don't bother. Jessie is still a child and much too young."

"Sir," Frémont braced himself, "we are already married. One month ago, Father James Cooke performed the ceremony for us in Georgetown."

"What!" Benton roared. "Married! I'll be damned! Get out of my house." He glowered at his daughter. "And as for you, young lady, get up to your room. I'll have this marriage annulled."

"No!" Jessie said sharply. She took Frémont's arm. "If John goes, I go."

For several moments, no one spoke. Then Benton sighed. "You wouldn't be a Benton if you didn't have that iron will," he grumbled. "I guess you win. Lieutenant Frémont—John, I mean—get your things and bring them here. You and Jessie can have the west wing of the house. I'd better go and tell Mrs. Benton the news." On the Senator's exit, the happy couple embraced.

With the United States only sixty years old, the lands from the west bank of the Mississippi to the shores of the Pacific were largely an unexplored wilderness. Except for a hardy breed of trappers and frontiersmen such as Kit Carson, Jim Bridger, and Etienne Provot, the Rocky Mountains remained a mystery to all but the Indians. The few sketchy maps that existed of this region, almost one-half the area of the United States, were far from accurate. Whole mountain ranges were missing, nonexistent rivers ran wildly through the Rockies, and actual streams escaped the mapmakers' attention entirely.

As settlers steadily moved westward from the Atlantic seaboard, the pressure for new farming land mounted. Expansionist politicians such as Benton were eager for the young republic to take a few giant steps west. Already competition with Britain for the Oregon country had reached the boiling point. The question of the latitudinal boundary of the United States became a major political slogan—"fifty-four-forty or fight."

What was needed was an accurate map showing the best routes to the fertile areas of the Pacific Northwest and California. Lewis and Clark had struck out for the Northwest, but their route was too far north and was passable only a few months in the year. With public enthusiasm fired by tales of the fabulous wealth of the West, Benton and his colleagues had no trouble in raising $30,000 to outfit a topographical expedition to be headed by Frémont.

In 1842, the lieutenant left Washington for St. Louis. One thing that impressed Frémont on the journey was the tidal wave of emigrants sweeping west. Already, a great Mormon congregation had settled in Nauvoo, Illinois. Real estate speculators, merchants, hunters, trappers, and entire families packed the Mississippi riverboats, heading west, where a man could stretch out, indulge his ambitions, and feel that material heaven might not be beyond his grasp.

In St. Louis, Frémont assembled his menage, which included his young brother-in-law Randolph; an expert topographer named Charles Preuss; a hunter, Lucien Maxwell; and a crew of rugged boatmen and woodsmen.

When he had completed his preparations for the expedition in St. Louis, Frémont made a short trip up the Missouri to their jumping-off point, near what is now Kansas City. Everything was in order, with one nagging exception—he still had no guide. The young leader pondered the problem as he idly watched water sloshing over the stern wheel. Suddenly, he was aware of a stocky fellow in the garb of a Mountain Man staring at him.

"Anything I can do for you?" the lieutenant inquired politely.

"No, but maybe I kin do somethin' for you," the frontiersman answered. "You Lieutenant Frémont? I hear tell you need a guide. Well, I think I know as much about that country as any man. I've fought the Injuns, and I ain't afeard, nohow."

Frémont liked the Mountain Man, from the straightforward look of his eyes to his well-knit body. "I am in need of a guide," he said cautiously. "What are your qualifications?"

"Well, I bin as far west as Californy, north to Oregon, south to Santa Fe. I've lived with Injuns and old Jim Bridger —if I could put up with an ornery cuss like Jim, I guess I can stand anybody. I cain't read or write, but I know how to get along in French and Spanish, and I never yet met Injuns I couldn't palaver with either in their own tongue or by sign language."

"*Quelle heure est il?*" Frémont casually asked.

"*Je ne sais pas,*" grinned the Mountain Man. "I don't own a timepiece."

After a few more such tests, Frémont was satisfied that the man was no idle braggart. They talked a little more about the lands to the west, and the Topographical Corps officer was greatly impressed by the man's knowledge. "You seem to know your business," Frémont said. "The pay is $125 a month, and we leave Kansas Landing in one week."

"I'll be ready," the newly-hired guide declared.

"One thing more. What is your name?" Frémont asked.

"Carson—Kit Carson" was the answer. And thus commenced a long friendship between Frémont and the famed frontiersman.

Carson was a member of a rare species of American—the Mountain Man. Rarely settling in any area for a lengthy period of time, the Mountain Men were rugged individualists, with a code of behavior uniquely their own. Possessed of great physical strength, shrewd enough to keep themselves alive in the face of nature's cruelest blows, they could be as savage as the Indians, and they generally took scalps when they fought the red man. They lived most of their lives in the wilderness, and their most remarkable trait was the ability to catalogue in their minds the territory they roamed and to recognize a landmark years later. Occasionally, memory played them false, as Frémont was to learn at horrible cost, but without their talents, thousands of settlers could never have made the perilous trip west.

This expedition, the first of five led by Frémont, was to gather information that would speed up emigration to the Columbia River Basin and pave the way for U.S. control of the Oregon Territory. Frémont was to map the country, pick out likely sites for military posts, and seek an easy route to the northwest territory. It was a six-month trip and took Frémont and his party through the South Pass and beyond the Continental Divide, deep into hostile Indian territory. Kit Carson considered the situation so dangerous that he made his will. Several men in the party quit when the intrepid lieutenant refused to turn back. In the following weeks, hardly a day passed that they did not encounter war parties of Blackfeet, Sioux, Cheyenne, and other hostile tribes. Always on guard and well-armed, the expedition traded with the savages, who exchanged fresh meat for beads or utensils. Sometimes, they would even stay with Frémont for a few days and act as guides.

On the trip back to St. Louis, Frémont attempted to make his way down the Platte River aboard a large rubber boat. The stream abruptly turned into a torrent, rushing between sheer cliffs and over treacherous rocks. As the boat gathered speed, three men on shore with safety lines attempted to slow it down, but the current was so swift that two of them had the rope jerked from their hands, and the third member, Basil Lajeunesse, was pulled headlong from a twelve-foot ledge into the churning waters. Although he was an expert swimmer, Lajeunesse bobbed helplessly in the water until, by luck, the rubber boat skittered into a calm eddy. Lajeunesse, half-drowned, was dragged over the gunwales.

A short while later, the rubber boat struck a submerged rock and catapulted men and equipment into the water. Three of them could not swim, but, by some miracle, all were saved. Most of the equipment was saved too, as it floated in wooden boxes a hundred yards below the accident. But all of their ammunition was lost, along with the sextant, telescope, and most of the guns.

When Frémont arrived back in Washington, he set to work on his report. The report discussed in detail important questions of topography, water, soil, vegetation, wild life, and weather. It was so skillfully done and so informative that it became the Bible of the pioneers.

But Frémont's first expedition had taken him only to the gates of the Oregon Territory. Immediately after his return to Washington, Frémont, his father-in-law, and other expansionists discussed a new project: exploring to the end of the Oregon Trail. There was plenty of support this time, and Frémont's second expedition was fitted out sumptuously with fine surveying instruments, a huge supply of trinkets for the Indians, superior new rifles, and ample provisions of food. There was even a howitzer that fired a twelve-pound ball.

Frémont tried to find a route to Oregon that lay further south than the way he had taken on his first trip. But even with the redoubtable Kit Carson blazing the trail, the terrain proved too severe. Forage for the animals and water became so scarce that the members of the party were forced to drink the putrid water from buffalo wallows.

The party forged on, moving north. The northern trails were jammed with hundreds of families moving westward, trappers with their Indian squaws, and an abundance of Indians looking for a chance to ambush straggling white men or steal from the emigrants.

After several months, Frémont reached Great Salt Lake, that vast salt water body discovered by the great scout Jim Bridger.

Frémont's report on the conditions around Great Salt Lake determined Brigham Young, four years later after the massacre of Mormons at Nauvoo, Illinois, to settle in Utah.

From Salt Lake, the expedition marched due north, all the way to what is now the state of Washington. The mission of the second expedition was now fulfilled, but Frémont was an ambitious man. Instead of heading back to Missouri, he decided to march south and explore the lands of the Sierra Nevadas, thereby circumscribing the entire huge northwest area of the United States.

Frémont was determined to cross the Sierra Nevadas and enter California. With no maps and no knowledge of what lay ahead of them, Frémont's party, in the dead of winter, plodded up the torturous Sierra Nevadas, through drifts of snow five feet deep. But Frémont doggedly went upward and onward. He was rewarded when they crested the range and looked down on the green valley of the Sacramento Basin.

Shortly thereafter, the expedition made its way to the fort of John Augustus Sutter, a man who was to become famous a few years later with the discovery of gold at Sutter's Mill.

Frémont spent but a short time in California and came away with a strong impression of Mexican misrule and the knowledge that there would be ample support for United States forces should they invade California.

The trip home took the expedition south through the Rockies. The path was fraught with danger, as war parties of starving Indians prowled the deserts of California and Nevada. One day, a Mexican and a young boy stumbled into camp with a tale of being ambushed by marauding Indians who had killed or captured four of their companions. Kit Carson and another Mountain Man, Alexander Godey, immediately decided to pursue the Indians and teach them a lesson. Tracking them by night, Carson and Godey brazenly charged the camp of thirty sleeping Indians. The savages, frightened by the piercing shrieks of the two white men, believed a much larger group was attacking them. Two Indians were shot down, and Carson and Godey returned to camp with the scalps swinging from their guns.

Whatever compunctions Frémont felt about scalp-taking by members of his group vanished the following day, when he came upon the remains of two of the Mexican men. Their bodies were savagely mutilated. Apparently, the two women, including the mother of the boy, had been carried off to the Indian lodges.

Blood-thirsty Ute Indians now followed the group like a pack of wolves waiting for stragglers. Several mules which fell behind disappeared. One of the men, named Tabeau, went back to look for them, and he too disappeared. Carson took up the trail and sadly reported, "The mule's dead and right next to his carcass, there's a puddle of blood. Tabeau must of gotten a couple of Ute arrows in his belly. The bushes down by the river are all broken up, so the Utes probably heaved his body into the water."

Tabeau's death marked the end of hardships, however, and Frémont returned to Washington without further mishap. The success of the expedition raised Frémont's stock tremendously. He received a double promotion, from second lieutenant to captain, and was on the road to being a public hero.

War clouds were now casting a darkening shadow from the Rio Grande to the Oregon Territory. Relations with the Mexican Government, which still regarded the Independent State of Texas as just a rebel province, were deteriorating rapidly, and the British in Canada were eyeing the Oregon Territory more covetously than ever. President Polk was willing to negotiate with Mexico over Texas, but he was fearful that the British, if they were permitted to move into Oregon, might eventually decide to extend their dominion all the way down through California. Under the circumstances, it was not difficult to get backing for a third expedition led by Frémont. The plan was to explore thoroughly the trails from Oregon to California, important in times of peace, crucial in case of war.

There seems little doubt that Frémont's expedition, aside from its scientific purpose, was considered a potential United States task force if war broke out. The party numbered sixty men. "I'll give a brand-new carbine to the twelve best shots," Frémont announced significantly, the first day on the trail, and he held marksmanship contests every day. The large party made excellent progress westward and crossed the mountains into California just before winter set in.

Frémont found the political pot in California just below the boiling point. He had several sharp diplomatic skirmishes with Mexican forces in the area, and his well-armed troop obviously troubled the local government. The commanding general in California finally sent a stiff note to Frémont, requesting him to quit the country immediately. Always impetuous, Frémont defied General Castro and prepared to do battle, hoisting an American flag over his position. General Castro issued a proclamation: "Frémont and his men are a band of robbers, and all loyal Californians will help us to expel them." Then he raised an army of two hundred men and prepared to storm Frémont's position. Unknown to Frémont, the United States and Mexico had already toppled over the brink on the question of Texas, and he began to have qualms about creating an incident which might start a war. Under cover of night, he evacuated his position and started north to Oregon. The expedition had only covered a few hundred miles, when a messenger reached Frémont with orders from Washington. Interpretations of these orders vary. Although they contained no explicit directions for the young captain to invade California, the courier carried verbal instructions that implied Frémont was free to act on his own judgment. Under the circumstances, the ambitious and impetuous young officer decided to drop the role of explorer and play soldier. That night he was so excited that he failed to post a guard about his camp.

As dawn began its slow unveiling, Kit Carson was awakened by the familiar horrible thump of a tomahawk splitting a skull. Before Carson could rouse the others, a howling band of Klamath Indians poured into the camp. One of Frémont's men, a Delaware Indian, fought bravely using his gun as a club, until he fell riddled with arrows. The white men finally drove off the Indians, bringing down the Klamath chief, but three of their own men lay dead and another wounded. Among those killed was the guide, Basil Lajeunesse. Kit

Carson in his anguish hacked the dead Klamath's chief's head to bits with his axe.

The survivors, bent on revenge, fell upon a large Klamath village the same day. Fourteen braves were slaughtered, and the Indians' annual supply of fish was destroyed. "A beautiful sight," Carson chortled vengefully. During the battle, the scout's life was saved by Frémont, when the captain, mounted on his horse, Sacramento, rode down a savage who was about to ambush Carson.

As Frémont marched into California, General Castro ordered all non-native Californians to leave the territory immediately. The effect was to rally recruits for Frémont's force.

Neither Frémont nor the American settlers in northern California were yet aware that a state of war had existed between Mexico and the United States for over a month. Frémont raided some Indian villages suspected of supplying mercenaries for Castro, and some settlers in the area surprised a small Mexican force and disarmed them. By now the settlers were determined to fight for independence. They captured the fort at Sonoma and then took over control of Sutter's Fort, despite the owner's obvious wish to stay out of the struggle. A flag bearing a star and a badly-drawn grizzly bear became the standard, and the little insurrection became known as the Bear Flag War. Frémont, along with the United States Naval forces in the area, still endeavored to appear neutral but it was impossible to disguise their sympathies. As skirmishes increased, Frémont found it necessary to actively take the field, ostensibly to keep the British from declaring a protectorate over California.

Very little blood had been spilled at this point, but finally news reached California of the outbreak of war between the United States and Mexico. Frémont, now reinforced with men from the United States Naval vessels, headed for Los Angeles. The city fell without a shot being fired, as the Mexican forces scattered in the face of the tiny but formidable force of Americans.

The conquering captain left Los Angeles and moved on to take Santa Barbara. In his absence, Los Angeles fell to a new Mexican force, and then was recaptured by forces under General Stephen Kearny, who had marched all the way from Santa Fe. Shortly thereafter, peace was made.

Frémont had been promoted to a lieutenant colonel, but up to this point, he had served under the command of Lieutenant Commander Stockton, a naval officer appointed by the Navy Department to secure California. When General Kearny arrived on the scene, he declared himself in charge. Stockton issued a proclamation making Frémont civil governor of the territory.

Kearny summoned Frémont. "You are to consider yourself under my command as of this moment. I am the governor of this territory, and you will take your orders from me!"

"My post has been awarded to me by Commander Stockton. Until I am notified differently, I will continue to obey his orders," Frémont replied angrily.

"You refuse to obey my direct order, Colonel Frémont," Kearny shouted.

"Until I am notified by Washington, I will continue to serve Commander Stockton."

"It's mutiny! I shall have you court-martialed. If I didn't know your father-in-law, I would have you shot on the spot."

"You have no right to charge me with mutiny," Frémont said, "and you'd better tell your men to keep their hands off me." With that, Frémont stomped out of the general's tent.

It was a serious error. Kearny's authority was eventually established by Washington, and he sent Frémont back to the nation's capital under arrest. Frémont's position was further jeopardized by Kearny's refusal to honor his debts incurred during the short war. This left Frémont holding the bag for $20,000 in notes guaranteed by his personal signature.

Back in Washington, one of the most famous courts-martial in American history began. Any hopes for discreetly settling the issue vanished, as a bitter Kearny insisted on making an example of Frémont, and an equally adamant Senator Benton demanded the right to erase the blot upon the record of his now famous son-in-law.

When it came time for Frémont to act as a witness in his

own behalf, he rose from the table where he sat with Senator Benton and addressed the court-martial: "General Brooke and other distinguished officers of this proceeding, I will make no attempt to raise technical or legal points in my defense. I am a soldier, not a lawyer, and I will speak in terms of my own profession." The explorer stopped and surveyed the crammed courtroom. The spectators included numerous officers resplendent in blue uniforms, a group of Indians interested in the mechanics of the white man's justice, and curious citizens from Washington society. He looked fondly at the Mountain Men in their own rough habits; they were sticking by their commander. His eyes hardened as he studied the stern features of General Kearny, so intent on a pound of flesh to salve his wounded pride.

In a well modulated tone, Frémont continued: "This trial is a comedy of errors. The first of these is the faulty orders sent out from Washington; second, the unjustifiable pretensions of General Kearny." Only a tiny shake of the young officer's head betrayed his contempt for his accuser. "And third, the conduct of the government in sustaining these pretensions. I consider this the greatest error."

These barbed remarks could hardly have been expected to sit well with the presiding officers, and certainly did not help Frémont's defense. When all of the fiery words had died away on both sides, Frémont was found guilty of three crimes: mutiny; disobedience of lawful commands of a superior officer; and conduct prejudicial to good order and discipline. The sentence: dismissal from the service.

The verdict of the court went to President Polk's cabinet for review, and upon the majority recommendation, Polk threw out the charge of mutiny, approved of the findings of the other two claims, but canceled any punishment. "Lieutenant Colonel Frémont . . . will resume his sword and report for duty," he ruled.

Frémont snapped back: "I refuse to accept the President's clemency. To accept means that I accede to the findings of the court-martial and am guilty. I am not guilty, and I hereby resign my commission in the Army."

Before leaving California, Frémont left $3,000 with an acquaintance to purchase some land. Now that he was out of the service, he determined to settle in the West. But first there remained one more crowning achievement to hurl in the face of his enemies. For several years, there had been talk of a transcontinental railway system. Ordinarily, the railroad line would have followed one of the southern routes across country, but friction between the North and South was mounting fast. The politicians decided that the railroad right-of-way ought to be as nearly central to the United States as possible, to avoid giving either North or South control over the railway.

Frémont's Fourth Expedition, numbering thirty-three men, set out for the Rockies to find a central pass in October, 1848. When they reached Pueblo, Colorado, Frémont was still without a guide; Kit Carson was unavailable for this venture. In Pueblo, he hired Old Bill Williams, a noted trapper and Mountain Man of the area, but certainly not the equal of the intelligent, farsighted Carson. Old Bill began his career as a missionary, but had switched trails to become a hard drinker, crack-shot, and unscrupulous dealer with Indians.

By the time the party reached the foot of the Rockies, they had been warned several times against attempting a central crossing in the winter. Indians returning from the mountains claimed that all signs pointed to the severest winter in history, but Frémont, determined to end his exploring career with a last great triumph, pushed on, with Old Bill marking the trail. As they clambered up the steep escarpments, snow piled up deeper and deeper. Game disappeared, and forage for the one hundred mules vanished. Prudent to the extreme when it came to provisioning the expedition, Frémont had stocked up enough corn to last the mules twenty-five days. Normally, the crossing, less than two hundred miles, could be made in about two weeks.

Snow drifts mounted, howling blizzards swept through the canyons. The snow, lashed by fierce winds, blotted out visibility, and it was difficult to breathe. At night, the men scooped out caverns in the snow and bedded down in little groups of four or five. Each morning they would be blanketed by a foot of snow, and it was a favorable day when the temperature went above zero. Using mauls and shovels, they broke paths for the mules foundering along in the belly-high snow. The days lengthened into weeks, and the feed for the mules began to run out.

Frémont called for Old Bill, "Are you certain you can find the pass?"

"I been in an' outta these mountains fer near thirty years," the guide snapped, "If you don't want to follow me, then to hell with yuh. I'll get on back to Pueblo."

A few days later, one of the men came back with good news. "I saw grass, maybe a day's march from here," he reported to Frémont, while Old Bill nodded triumphantly. A day later, they reached the "grass."

"My God!" cried one of the men. "That's not grass. It's the tops of trees sticking up out of thirty feet of snow."

The cold ate into the mules' thin bodies, and one by one they began toppling over dead. When the hunger of the men became unbearable, they ate the dead mules.

During a monstrous storm that kept them from moving more than a few feet an hour, Frémont turned to Old Bill. "Apparently your knowledge of the Rockies is not what we supposed. You've led us up a blind alley. We must retreat to the river." The expedition began the slow march back, discarding equipment along the trail like a defeated army.

Down the rugged cliffs, they stumbled. Frostbite blackened their toes. They waded through swift-moving streams, up to their armpits in frigid water, and their clothes froze to their limbs. Ice stiffened their beards and crusted their eyebrows; snow formed epaulets upon their shoulders; and hunger pangs gnawed at every belly.

The situation was desperate. Frémont called for four volunteers. Old Bill, King, Breckenridge, and Creutzfeldt stepped forward. "Try to get through to the settlement at Taos and get help," he told them.

Traveling lightly, with only a single blanket apiece, the

four volunteers slipped away. The rest of the expedition set up a camp and grubbed for food. They even boiled their rawhide ropes to make a gluey soup. They waited a week, then two weeks, and still there was no sign of rescue.

"I'm afraid the Indians have intercepted our men," Frémont announced gloomily. "I'll take four men and head for Taos myself tomorrow. If all goes well, we'll be back within a fortnight."

Frémont and his companions had traveled but a short way downriver when they met some friendly Indians. The two groups began traveling together. A few days later, they saw smoke rising from a clump of trees. Edging up cautiously, Frémont and his group came to a clearing. "It's Bill and the others," Godey yelled and leaped into the clearing. The condition of the three men around the fire was pitiful. Emaciated as scarecrows, they were scarcely able to move. After they had been given a little water and some food, Frémont questioned them about the missing fourth man.

Old Bill stared stonily into the woods. Breckenridge whispered, "He's dead. He collapsed from starvation at our last camp a couple of miles back." As Frémont and the others listened, Breckenridge added, "We were lucky. Right after he died, we shot a deer."

Frémont and Godey went back up the river a way until they found the camp where King's body lay. Big chunks of flesh had been hacked off of it. Godey stared at the mutilated corpse in horror. "They didn't kill any damn deer."

"Cannibals, cannibals," murmured the shocked Frémont. But he could not bring himself to confront Breckenridge or Old Bill with their crime when he returned to the other camp; they were too delirious to realize what they had done.

The three living skeletons were tied to horses borrowed from the Indians and taken to a settlement at Red River, and a relief party under Alexander Godey was sent back to get the other members of the party. These unfortunate wretches had decided not to wait, and had struck out down the river. Many of them died on the trail. Others were left behind to die beside a fire. Madness struck some, and they wandered off into the woods, never to be seen again. All semblance of comradeship vanished, and it was every man for himself. They ate anything they could find: a dead wolf, right down to the entrails, dried buds on bushes, and even water bugs. When the rescuers met them, a total of eleven men had perished, and the living ones were ragged scarecrows who had to be lifted off the mules that brought them to the settlement.

Frémont himself suffered a badly frozen leg, but what hurt him far more was the realization that he had failed miserably in his quest and that his faulty judgment was partially responsible for the deaths of eleven men. Repeatedly, he had been warned not to attempt the crossing in the winter. Also, his failure to order an earlier retreat from the mountains was a fatal error. In his usual proud manner, however, he refused to admit his defeat and wrote that the expedition had been a success—a classic masterpiece in self-delusion.

Jessie had preceded him by boat to California, where to his dismay, Frémont found that his agent had purchased a large piece of desolate land at Mariposa instead of the piece he had specified. Grimly, he set to work, trying to develop a profitable farm.

Meanwhile, gold was discovered at Sutter's Mill, and now the trickle of settlers into California swelled to a mighty river of men with gold fever. Frémont hired experienced miners to try his property, and hit a bonanza. Other prospectors poured onto Frémont's holdings because of a law which did not give a man title to mineral rights on property he purchased. However, there was plenty of the precious metal to go around, and within a few years, Frémont had taken ten million dollars out of the ground.

Once California was admitted to the Union, Frémont became a natural candidate for the Senate. In 1850, he sat in the capitol as the first senator from the Golden State. His term was uneventful, and when he returned to California, he immediately ran into financial reversals.

Embroiled in lawsuits, Frémont returned to his beloved

profession of exploration. Once again, the purpose was to find a central route through the Rockies. With a well-outfitted expedition, Frémont set forth into the mountains which had almost been his tomb. The pathfinder took no guide along this trip, but he did have the first official photographer ever attached to an exploring expedition, Solomon N. Carvalho.

Despite the great caution Frémont exercised on this venture, the party soon found itself in serious trouble when it got up into the mountains. The men had to eat their horses and mules when they became snowbound on the steep slopes and to sleep in holes dug out of the icy drifts.

Fortunately the group managed to make a Mormon settlement in Utah with only one casualty.

Frémont's work as an explorer was now finished. His name still ranked high in public esteem, and a number of political factions began to consider him Presidential timber. Finding the anti-slavery platform of the newly-formed Republican Party to his liking, Frémont, in 1856, became that party's first Presidential candidate.

He was subjected to vicious attacks by the Democrats. He was accused of being a boozer, maligned as a slave-holder, berated as a financial swindler, and castigated as being cruel and rapacious in his treatment of Californians during the Bear Flag War. The most telling argument against Frémont, however, was that a victory for him meant secession by the South. A flamboyant opposition orator howled, "Frémont is a damned abolitionist. Tell me if the hoisting of the black flag over you by a Frenchman's bastard is not an act of war!"

When the sound and fury was over and the ballots were counted, Buchanan emerged as President.

Frémont now turned his attention to Mariposa and his financial problems. He was in Europe attempting to sell shares in his estate to pay off debts when Southern soldiers touched off their cannons at Fort Sumter. Lincoln appointed Frémont one of the leading Union generals, and he became commander of the Department of the West, Illinois, and all the states and territories between the Mississippi and the Rockies.

No general ever started off behind a bigger military eight

ball. Headquarters were in St. Louis, where most of the people sided with the South, and Confederate troops were openly recruited. In this nest of spies and enemies, Frémont took up residence. Personally, he was ill-fitted for such a campaign. Almost his entire military career had been spent in exploration. He knew nothing of tactics and the manipulation of large armies. His troops were untrained, many of them ninety-day volunteers who simply quit and went home when their terms expired. The equipment was abominable. His subordinate generals thought in terms of personal glory, and if the battle plans didn't suit them, they were content to sulk in their tents and let somebody else do the shooting.

Guerilla warfare broke out in the territory, and Southern armies had a field day as Frémont's armies panicked in retreat or else attacked in foolhardy bravado, which cost thousands of lives. Criticism was poured on the unlucky commander's head, and his personal aloofness did nothing to increase his popularity. Charges of extravagance smeared Frémont, and his issuance of an administrative order freeing slaves in his territory two years before the President's Emancipation Proclamation alienated Lincoln.

Alarmed by the deterioration of relations between Frémont and Lincoln, Jessie set off for Washington. In a personal interview with the President, she pleaded her husband's case so forcefully that Lincoln agreed to give Frémont further opportunity to prove himself worthy of his command.

At the time, Frémont was embarked upon a campaign south toward New Orleans. The President wrote to General Curtis in St. Louis: "Here are orders relieving General Frémont of his command. But understand this, General Frémont is now on a campaign south toward New Orleans. He has hopes of a decisive battle within the next few days. If, when you arrive in his sector, you find him to have won a battle or be engaged in a great battle or on the verge of one with the enemy, you are to withhold the relief order until further word from me."

It was to no avail. Frémont's decisive battle never took place. His equipment fell apart, his intelligence proved faulty, and his subordinate generals continued to backbite and drag their heels.

Frémont in his one hundred days of command was not a total failure, however. His huge railroad station built in St. Louis later proved invaluable to the Union cause; he had held most of his territory. He had also given a little known general from Illinois an opportunity to demonstrate his skill; the officer was Ulysses S. Grant.

Frémont in 1863 was given another military command, in the Virginia mountain section, but again his ignorance of tactics proved fatal. Stonewall Jackson proceeded to give him such a lesson in the science of war that Lincoln was forced to relieve Frémont once more.

When the war ended, Frémont entered into a railroad building scheme. Selling out his Mariposa holdings, he paid off his debts and put all his remaining money into the newly-formed Atlantic and Pacific Railway. His partners raised considerable capital in Europe by misrepresenting their enterprise. They told investors that the railroad was in operation and that the federal government guaranteed the interest on the railroad's bonds. When the entire scheme collapsed, Frémont went bankrupt and barely escaped prison.

Frémont was past sixty now, with three children and a wife to support. Jessie chipped in by becoming a professional writer, and Congress provided charity in the form of the governorship of the Arizona Territory at a salary of $2,000 a year. It was a bitter comedown for a man who twenty years earlier had been worth ten million.

In 1890, the government reappointed Frémont major general, with retirement pay of $6,000. Shortly after, he came to New York to settle some business affairs. He took sick in a Manhattan boarding house and died of peritonitis.

When the news was brought to Jessie in California, she sat and stared out the window toward the ocean. Without tears, she pronounced her husband's epitaph: "From the ashes of his campfires sprung cities."

The Kit Carson Nobody Knows

Other mountain men might shoot straighter, fight harder, and guide better, but all the pioneers looked up to this homely runt, because there wasn't anything too big for him to handle

By the time he was thirty-five, Kit Carson was already a legend, and down through the years, the stories of his exploits have grown with the telling, until many people think of him now as a bull-chested, massive-shouldered, swashbuckling, two hundred-pound mountain of a man with a voice like thunder. Actually, Kit Carson never weighed more than 135 pounds, and he was barely five feet, seven inches tall and thick in the middle. His short legs were bowed like barrel staves. His eyes were normally dull gray, his plain face a bit solemn, his voice thin and high. He was never reckless, boastful, or aggressive, but always painfully shy and modest. Yet there was within this odd-looking little man a special kind of self-confidence and competence that commanded instant respect and won him high esteem wherever he went. Because of that, the real Kit Carson and the manner in which he became a fabulous character are far more interesting than all the myths that grew around him.

His mother, Rebecca, was a haughty Virginian; and his father, Lindsey Carson, was a tall Scotch-Irishman, who fought Indians in the Carolinas and Kentucky before settling down in the outpost town of Franklin, Missouri. When Lindsey died, he left Rebecca with ten children, all husky except Kit, who was her fifth child and a runt.

When Kit was fifteen, Rebecca bound him over as an apprentice to Dave Workman, the saddler, in the hope that once he had learned a profitable trade, he'd climb right on up until he became a banker. But Kit "had the hair of the black bear in him," as Tom Fitzpatrick, the famous trapper, said the first time he laid eyes on him. So before Kit's first year at the saddlery was up, Dave Workman knew well enough what kind of a wild sprout he had on his hands. And, being the kind of a man he was, he did the right thing about it. One day he drew Kit into his back room and said: "Your time's come, lad. You got to clear out of here. You sign on with the Santa Fe caravan tomorrow—you and Andy Broadus. Charles Bent wants Andy as teamster and a cub to help him. You take my Hawken."

Kit was eager to go, all right, but worried about what his mother would say to Dave when she missed him. "Don't you fret about that," Dave said. "We'll pull the wool over her eyes. Look at this." And he showed Kit an advertisement he was inserting in the *Intelligencer,* which said:

Notice is hereby given to all persons that Christopher Carson, a boy about sixteen years old, small for his age, light hair, ran away from the subscriber to whom he had been bound, on or about the first of September, 1826. He is supposed to have made his way to the upper part of the state. All persons are notified not to harbor, support, or assist said boy under

penalty of the law. One cent reward will be given to any
person who will bring back said boy. Signed, David Workman.

The next dawn Kit rode a wheel mule, not north as Dave's
ad would suggest, but southwest with the Bent caravan of sixty
men and eighteen hooped wagons. It made him a little sad to
think of Rebecca, but he didn't think of her long or often. He
was as happy now as a caged bird let loose. He was free. Nobody would have a right to call him a pork-eater much longer.
Pretty soon he'd be out of these teamster duds and into buckskins and moccasins. Then everybody would know him for a
Mountain Man!

One day as they toiled along the trail, Andy Broadus mis-
handled his gun and sent a ball ripping up his own arm.
Gangrene developed, and Andy began slipping toward an
anguished death. He was a good man, kind to Kit, and generous. Charles Bent called for a volunteer to amputate. Nobody
came forward.

In the crisis, Kit doodled in the dust, as he recalled an
awful morning when he had watched his father hack off the
infected arm of a neighbor. He remembered the process. He
knew he could do it himself, but he wished a man would step
up, because the mere thought of the ordeal terrified him. He
could do what had to be done, though, and he must do it.

"Mr. Bent," he said, in a small, soft voice, "if they's no one
else, I'll cut off Andy's arm."

Charles Bent was nobody's fool. He was the grandson of
Silas Bent, who led the Boston Tea Party; he had been edu-
cated at West Point; he would become, one day, the first
governor of New Mexico. He stared at Kit a long moment. At
first he saw merely a rash teenager, pretending not to be afraid.
Then he saw something else in the wide stubborn mouth, the
gray eyes turning turquoise. He recognized the outer symptoms
of an indomitable will.

Bent crooked a finger at Kit and called for the knives, the
saw, the kingbolt glowing red in the forge. Somebody poured
rum down Andy's throat until he was numb. Then Kit went to
work with the caravan crowd huddled around tense and fear-

ful. He retched when Andy screamed and retched again sawing the bone with Andy's blood spurting over him. But his hands were quick and steady. After cauterizing the wound with the kingbolt and dressing it with tar, he felt Andy's pulse and found, to his immeasurable relief, that it was still strong.

So the caravan moved on, and one crisp, clear November morning, Kit gazed for the first time on Santa Fe, mountain-girded in a blaze of sunshine—hundreds of low white adobe buildings and the towers of a pink church. Bubbling brown children escorted *los Americanos* down the Camino del Alamo past doorways in which senoritas in flowered blouses and flaring skirts stood waving. Many of these ran to the teamsters and were hefted up behind them astride the mules.

In the dusty plaza, Kit saw Indian slaves being sold at auction, grog-stands, and faro tables aswarm with Mexican soldiers. He gaped at the governor's long adobe palace and shyly greeted old friends from Franklin—Ewing Young, the big, genial captain of trappers, and old Kincaid in tattered buckskins. Both Mountain Men had homes in Taos and were down for the fandangos which accompanied the infrequent arrival of caravans from the States.

Kincaid sent Kit to Gertrudes Barcelo's *casa* in Burro Alley to seek lodging, until Bent sold his goods and paid his men. Kit found Gertrudes in her patio watching a cockfight—a tall, handsome young woman in a short red skirt and a brief, tight chemisette, with a paper rose tucked behind a small golden ear. She smoked a corn-husk *cigarillo,* and she seemed to glow as though lighted inside. Her full lips and the toe nails of her bare feet were vermilion, and her long legs were bronzed and shapely. Women in Franklin used yards of calico to hide how they were put together below the neck. Not Gertrudes. She displayed her body with pride.

Taking Kit's hand, she enchanted him and warmed him, as she led him to her common room, where she assigned him sleeping space among the serapes lining the walls. Then she drew him quite close to her and gently but casually whispered a startling proposition that made Kit blush purple and stammer: "No thank you, ma'am." Gertrudes took no offense. She patted his cheek and said, "*Esta bien,* leetle pork-eater. I wait. You be a Mountain Man one day, and then you will come to me."

In the blurry week that followed—a week of dancing and flirting, gambling, guzzling aguardiente, and stuffing down frijoles and tortillas—Kit got rid of the entire eight dollars which Bent paid him for two months of mule driving. He exchanged his teamster homespuns for buckskins, but made no other progress toward becoming a Mountain Man.

Once Ewing Young told him, "You're too small for gettin' up to beaver, bub. Them fellows would laugh in your face." How Kit hated Ewing's contemptuous "bub." Twice he started home in black despair—and twice was drawn back. He spent the winter cooking for Young and dumping slops. And then one day, when he'd made up his mind the third time to turn tail and go back to Dave's saddlery, Ewing Young came in and said one of his trappers had gotten into a fight with a girl who had stabbed him and dumped him in the town cesspool, hurt bad. Ewing dropped a Newhouse trap at Kit's feet and commanded him to try setting it. Kit fell upon it and did set the stiff six-inch jaws, though with difficulty. Ewing scratched his stubby chin: "You come along with me on the fall hunt, bub, if you want to. But I'll only be taking you halfway. Then you'll have to help tote back the skins to lighten the load."

As Kit rode out of Taos with the Young party, he was dizzy with delight, and he wished Gertrudes Barcelo could see her "leetle pork-eater" now. No pork any more for Kit, or any other greenhorn luxury; from now on he would take his living off the land. He was a genuine trapper and Mountain Man at last.

Young's first objective was the Salt River in the White Mountains of what is now Arizona. At its headwaters there was an Indian sign—Apaches, Young said. At dawn the next day, while on sentry duty, Kit observed a nervous stirring of mules and a yakking of magpies. Spotting a hundred or more Apaches on foot slipping down a ridge, he woke Young, who roused the camp, got it ready to move, and laid an ambush. Young placed Kit and the smaller men outside the pack train.

The rest walked crouching in the center of it, hidden by the mules. From afar the party would appear to be a few unprotected traders, perhaps heading for the Santa Rita copper mine.

It must have looked good to the Apache chiefs. Kit saw them signal a charge, and the long line of naked, painted men moved forward armed with spears and bows. When they were a hundred yards off, Young told his front line to blaze away. Kit aimed above the heart of a tall chief, fired, missed. He spat another ball into his muzzle, rammed it, primed, and fired again. This time the chief flung his arms high and toppled. One brass tack for Kit's gun stock!

After the Apaches scattered up the ridge, leaving seven of their men killed, Kit hurried toward his dead chief. It was his first kill and he wanted that glossy black scalp to hang on his leggings. But Ewing Young was there ahead of him, and began circling the skull with his knife. Kit watched a moment as the big man yanked at the hair, at Kit's property, Kit's prize. Something flamed inside him, raw anger at Young's unfairness. His eyes turned turquoise. His voice came out piercing and peremptory. "Drop it!" Kit shouted. "That thar's mine!"

It was a command. The captain whirled in astonishment. He peered at the small enraged figure before him. And he released the hair. Kit jumped in, grabbed it, placed a moccasined foot on the chief's blue-painted face, and jerked. The scalp came away with a loud pop and Kit stuffed the bloody trophy in his belt.

He glanced at Young then, suddenly appalled by his behavior. He was a shy boy again. But that uncontrollable moment of command was characteristic. Even in his teens, by the power of his personality Kit could dominate absolutely. And it was all right. Young began to laugh. Then he sputtered, "Good for you, Kit! You earned that topknot for sure and you taught me a lesson. Thought for a mite you aimed to take my hair too!"

No "bub" this time!

Thereafter the Young party trapped in peace down the lovely Salt River and north up the Verde. Kit was trapping badly, spoiling ponds by leaving scent on beaver slide and bait stick. Smart beaver sprung his traps, buried them, or ran

off with his float. It was provoking, but Kit could not be mad
at the beavers. Their intelligence delighted him, and each
day he learned something from them.

Buffalo was the food staple of the western wilderness.
Cottonwoods gave shelter and winter forage. But beaver pelts,
in demand for hats the world over, were money. With pelts,
the Mountain Man bought the tools of his craft—guns, traps,
knives, mules. With pelts he hired squaws to make his clothes
and lodges. Pelts gave him cash for gambling, drinking, tobacco, and love.

By February, when they reached the source of the Verde,
Kit's trapping had improved so much he was getting three
beaver in five tries, which was better than average. It was
time now for Young to split his brigade, sending half his men
back with $13,000 worth of pelts. The lucky rest would be
the very first ever to attempt a trapping trip to California—
that golden land of the Spaniard so remote as to seem almost
a myth.

Kit awaited Young's order for him to return home, as had
been specified when he was hired, but the order never came.
Instead Young not only included him in the select twenty for
the great western adventure, but also put him in charge of the
rear. That made him Lieutenant Carson, second in command!

For ten days the reduced party toiled over an arid plateau
to the Colorado River, where the starved men feasted on a
fat mare and her tender unborn foal, gifts of the Mohave
Indians. Some of the men were hungry for women too, and
the polite chief produced a flock of black-banged girls with
solid little bodies, ecstatic over the chance to prove their
value while earning a few trinkets. The party moved on
across the burning Mohave Desert, which turned Kit's skin
almost black and nearly blinded him before they came down
through Cajon Pass into Southern California. Beaver were
abundant along the San Joaquin River, and the whole region
was a paradise of game. The Americans summered below San
Francisco Bay hard by the San Jose Mission, and Kit, ap-
proaching twenty-one, gained weight on fat beef and Spanish
brandy. In that subdued atmosphere, the men again grew

restive for love, so when he broke camp in September, Young headed for Los Angeles, which was a pleasure village—and for a full rowdy week the adobe shacks resounded with joyous sounds.

In Los Angeles, Big Jim Lawrence went berserk when Little James Higgins' adoring senorita, Dolores, refused to extend to him also her tender favors. Ripping her clothes apart and stripping her down to her chemise, he spit on her and mauled her unmercifully. That started a violent altercation between the two Mountain Men, which reached its bloody climax some days later on the trail. The trappers had just come across a battalion of Mexican soldiers, a mean-looking crew on the prod for mischief; and when Young halted his party to size up the situation, Big Jim's rabidly inflamed mind suddenly hit on having it out then and there with Little James. Gun ready, Big Jim dug his heels into his mount and was plunging up abreast of the smaller man, when Higgins jerked his mule broadside of Lawrence's path, snapped up his rifle, and fired into the ugly giant's sneering face, ripping out the back of his head and sending him tumbling to the ground. Then the victor calmly dismounted, scalped the vanquished, and tied the dripping trophy to his wiper stick. That was too much for the bold but queasy Mexicans—they scampered south like scared rabbits. But Kit didn't find it revolting. Justice in the wilderness might sometimes be grisly—yet it was fair.

After recrossing the Mohave, Young and his men trapped through the fall down the Colorado to tidewater and up the Gila. Captain Young and Kit hurried on ahead to Taos to report their epic return from California.

Kit hurried for another reason. Gertrudes Barcelo was doing business in Taos these days, and he yearned to show her what his eighteen-month trip had done for her "leetle pork-eater." His buckskins and ragged felt hat were shiny with grease. His hair, cropped at the neck, was matted with the dirt of the trail. He had acquired a taste, if hungry enough, for ants, snakes, and skunk. He could throw a fast pack hitch, kill a deer at fifty yards if not hurried, handle most mules, keep dry in wet weather, and smell Indians. He weighed 130 pounds, and he was man enough now not to be bashful when a senorita made sly remarks and bold propositions.

And so it was that worldly-wise Gertrudes—after giving him a hot bath and combing the rubbish out of his matted hair—had the pleasure of finally making a man out of him.

On Young's recommendation, Kit was included in another trapping crew organized by Thomas Fitzpatrick. In mid-September, 1831, the Fitzpatrick brigade rode north from Taos through the golden aspens, up the San Luiz and Wet Mountain valleys, across the Colorado parks along the Continental Divide, and into the Laramie Plains. They ascended the Sweetwater, crossed South Pass to Green River, and went northward to Jackson's Hole beneath the Tetons. Fitzpatrick told Kit those impressive protuberances were named by a homesick Spanish trapper, in honor of a faraway sweetheart.

This majestic country was the land of Kit's dreams, but when the hunt ended that fall, he decided to leave Fitzpatrick's brigade and go it alone. So he paid Tom what he owed on his trapping outfit and pointed his mules toward Teton Pass, embarking on his career as the freest of all mountaineers, the free trapper. Wintering in Pierre's Hole, he left for Taos in the spring, pausing at the Arkansas River to see the great trading fort which Charles and William Bent had built in partnership with the elegant Ceran St. Vrain of New Orleans. For a day he suffered from violent love of St. Vrain's visiting relative, fifteen-year-old Felicité, a piquant doll who wore so many bustles and pads that Kid couldn't tell what was girl and what wasn't.

His moccasins were in shreds, so he asked Felicité to sew him a pair. She called him *cochon* and announced that blue-blooded French beauties were too refined to work. So Kit crossed the river to the Arapahoe village and sat glumly in the tepee of Chief Running-Around-In-A-Circle while his daughter, Grass Singing, cut the moccasins.

As Kit paid for them, he forgot Felicité a moment and looked at Grass Singing. Her beauty struck him like sudden pain. He saw a brown-eyed, small-featured, slender girl in a bright calico blouse and knee-length doeskin skirt decorated with pressed quills. She smelled of health and cleanliness, and also of sage and other pleasant herbs.

Confused by her charms, Kit offered her a silver dollar. Grass Singing misunderstood. She thought that this stocky little white hunter was trying to buy her for a few minutes. She threatened him with her fists, one of which held an awl, driving him from the tepee.

For some months Kit worked with John Gantt's outfit, which forted up for winter on the Arkansas near today's Pueblo, Colorado. One bitter January morning, Kit found that nine horses had been run off by Crow Indians toward Pikes Peak. With ten others he trailed the thieves up Fountain Creek all day through the howling wind and swirling snow. Kit had forgotten his underwear, and his buckskins froze to his thighs. At twilight he spotted the Crow camp near the base of the great mountain.

Picketing their mounts, the trappers spent four hours crawling forward until they were close enough to the Crows for Kit to count fifty of them, stark naked in the sub-zero weather, dancing and feasting around two fires. The nine stolen horses were picketed near them. Soon they stopped cavorting and crawled into two small brush forts to sleep. Kit and four benumbed companions slipped up, freed the nine horses, and drove them with snowballs back to their own mounts. The Crows and their dogs heard nothing because of the wind.

With their property recovered, most of the trappers wanted to ride back to Pueblo out of this awful discomfort. Kit argued against it. In the wilderness, where horses were as vital for survival as guns, to steal them was a much worse offense than murder. Those Crows had to be taught a lesson. So the weary party returned to the Indian camp, and battled the thieves until the first glow of dawn appeared on Pikes Peak. Five of the fifty Indians were killed, and Kit judged this to be proper punishment.

As the willows yellowed with spring along the Arkansas, Kit grew restless. He was dreaming of women a lot lately, —sometimes of the much-padded Felicité St. Vrain, sometimes of the voluptuous Gertrudes Barcelo, but most of all of Grass Singing, though he didn't call her that. He didn't care much for Indian names, so he called her Alice. She stayed in his mind as he trailed with Gantt up Ute Pass around Pikes Peak, across South Park and the Mosquitoes to the Upper Arkansas, sparkling blue and swift-running beneath the snows of the Sawatch Range. When Gantt released Kit in the fall, he hurried to Bent's Fort hoping to find Alice in her village. No luck. She was in the Green River country with her father.

He moved gloomily down to Taos, lost a thousand dollars at monte in a week, borrowed supplies and a train of trader's goods from Charles Bent, and lit out for Green River. He hunted Alice on the Green, the White, and the Uintah, and wintered disconsolately at the Utah post of Antoine Roubidoux. A moderate drinker as a rule, Kit put away plenty of Antoine's raw alcohol that winter.

One March day, there arrived at Fort Roubidoux from California a tall, darkhaired scamp of a trapper from Virginia, Joe Meek. About Kit's age, Joe was in love with a Shoshone girl named Mountain Lamb, who was unfortunately the wife of his good friend Milton Sublette. For ever so long, Kit listened to Joe telling how fine it was to have a sturdy little Indian girl for a wife. A man would find it mighty nice having her to raise and strike his lodge, bathe his cracked feet, light his pipe, keep the fire going, dress hides, and darn leggings. On the trail, she'd be close behind him on her little mule, quick to sense danger. At siesta she'd be happy to hold his tired head in her lap, and brush the mosquitoes away.

When Joe finally paused for breath, Kit shyly mentioned that he had just such a girl in mind, the daughter of Chief Running-Around-In-A-Circle down at Bent's.

Joe was thrilled. "Let's go, Kit!" he exclaimed. "Let's go find her right now! Time's a-wastin'—and you twenty-five years old! I'd give a million beaver if I could have Mountain Lamb. You can have your girl. Let's go!"

Bent's Fort and Alice were a month's trek from Port Roubidoux. But Kid and Joe hit the Old Spanish Trail through southern Utah and upper New Mexico, reaching Bent's in mid-June of 1834. Shyer than ever, now that Alice was nearby, Kit thought he ought to go to her father, tell him how much he loved her, and offer to buy her for his spare Hawken, plus an old mule with soft feet. When he outlined his plan to Joe Meek and William Bent, Charles Bent's younger brother, they vetoed it with scorn. The price he was offering was much too high. Taking him in hand, they hauled him between them to the Arapahoe village.

After arranging an audience with Chief Running-Around-In-A-Circle, they disrobed Kit to prove that he was as sound as a dollar. Then they demanded that Alice submit also to a physical examination.

When the chief called Alice into his tepee, she agreed to the examination, thinking it would only be a routine poking, inspection of teeth, nose, and ears, and listening to her heart. But Meek and Bent were set on doing a thorough job. Grabbing hold of Alice, they shoved her back on a big drum and started taking off her blouse and doeskin skirt. That was too much for the proud and spunky little Indian princess. She kicked and scratched, and in next to no time she had the tepee all to herself. As for marrying Little Chief, which was what the Indians called Kit Carson, she wasn't going to let herself be bought for any bargain price of one Hawken and an old mule with soft feet. If Little Chief wanted her, she announced in shrill Arapahoe, the price was twenty-five horses.

Twenty-five horses! That came to a thousand dollars!

When Bill Mitchell, a trapper friend, learned of Kit's sad plight, he said the best way to get hold of a thousand dollars in a hurry was by finding a gold mine—and he offered to guide Kit to a likely spot. On hearing that, Joe Meek had a sudden attack of gold fever too, and the three of them set out the next morning with six mules and three husky Shawnees for the desolate Cimarron water-scrape. But they didn't find any gold there, and it wasn't long before they were almost out of water, sick from the beating sun and worried about signs that a Comanche war party was about. Wearily they turned the mules toward the purple Spanish Peaks far to the west.

The gift, or perhaps the burden, of leadership is a strange thing. Of those six men on that arid barren, Kit was much the smallest, the weakest, and the least imposing. Yet when scouts of the Comanche war party showed their painted bodies over a ridge, the others all turned to Kit, and without a word being spoken he was instantly nominated to take charge.

Sharply, he ordered the mules picketed, the packs dumped close in. As he watched some two hundred Comanche warriors assemble on the ridge, forming a forest of lances and bows, he warned his five to check their powder and lead and prime their rifles. His wide mouth pursed wryly as howls went up from chiefs and medicine men who approached to inspect them just out of gun range. Those howls meant that inhuman tortures would surely follow a Comanche victory—perhaps slow death by roasting, suspended head down over a small fire. It was mid-morning, twelve hours until dark. While the head medicine man chanted, screamed, and shook his rattle, the long line of mounted Indians moved down from the ridge and circled the Carson party, slowly at first and then faster, narrowing the circle. These unprotected palefaces wouldn't have time to dig in.

Kit pondered. Their six slow mules could never outrun the split-eared Spanish horses of the Comanches. He gave an order, and the other five nodded. The mules were moved head to tail in their own small circle. Kit called "Ready!" Each man cut the throat of his mule and guided its dying body to the sand. Before the Comanches were close enough to use their bows, Carson and Company were safe behind Fort Mule.

The terrible hours of sporadic battle wore on. Kit killed the first head medicine man, and the Comanches retired to choose another. Joe Meek killed the second and third medicine men, causing delays for more elections which gave the

Carson men some rest and saved their ammunition. But the awful heat, the buzzing flies, the throat-burning dust, made life hard to bear in Fort Mule. Carson doled out water drop by drop. His skin and that of his companions rose in blisters. Their ears ached from the incessant shrieks of the warriors and the laments of their squaws carrying off the dead.

Sunset came, coolness, twilight, darkness. Fort Mule on its outer surfaces was so full of arrows, Kit couldn't find a hand-sized space. Joe Meek estimated forty Comanches had been killed. The chiefs seemed aware of the extent of their disaster as they broke the war circle and moved up the ridge to camp for the night. Fort Mule's defenders heard their chants for revenge and the yells of the current medicine man promising that these white devils could not escape. In the morning things would be different.

As the chiefs chanted, Kit put one Shawnee to wriggling on his belly away from Fort Mule, his progress covered by the rifles of the others. A second Shawnee wriggled off ten minutes later, and then the third. Mitchell, Meek, and Carson followed in turn. The Comanche lookouts didn't spot them. Two miles from Fort Mule, the six men paused and soothed their raw bellies with bear grease. Then abandoning guns, knives, powder, lead, and what little was left of their clothes, they began moving west at a slow, steady dogtrot.

They trotted all night. In ten hours they covered seventy-five miles, reaching water and Rocky Mountain foothills before sunrise, and disappearing gratefully into the pine and cedar forest. They were almost done in, and their bare feet were bloody. They didn't care. Kit didn't even mind walking into the busy square at Bent's Fort ludicrously naked and without any gold. Life was sweeter than all the gold on earth. And there must be easier ways to win Alice.

After a week's rest, Kit and Joe Meek left Bent's, joining Jim Bridger beyond South Pass. Alice and her Arapahoe village were supposed to be somewhere ahead of them. They trapped above Pierre's Hole, skirmishing constantly with Blackfeet. They wintered on Henry's Fork of the Snake and spent spring trying to trap in the tributaries of the Green

River. The sly Sioux were thick in the area, and they lost a dozen mules. In mid-June of 1835, Kit and Joe moved on to the Green River rendezvous.

The rendezvous was a bright city of white and yellow buffalo-skin lodges, thronged with buckskinned trappers and redskins. The area crawled with dogs, bear cubs, pet deer, and naked Indian children. Kit figured two thousand people were there ready to trade furs and hides for the store goods packed out from Independence and St. Louis. Business, however, would occupy them briefly. Most of them were there to let off steam after many months of dull routine and tiresome danger. They were there to race and shoot, brawl and boast, gorge and gamble and flirt, bed with squaws, and drink firewater.

After searching in vain for Alice, Kit went off to bathe in Green River. Undressing on the grassy bank, he was washing in a pool, when he heard laughter and splashings above him. He pushed upstream and waded around the bank, where a dozen nude Indian girls were bathing, sluicing each other, and playing tag. One of them, slender, smallboned, and goldtinted, scrambled on the bank to dive. It was Alice, and just as she dove, she recognized Little Chief standing hip-deep in the water. Gurgling as she came up, she hurled a handful of gravel in his direction and he sank under water in panic, swimming back around the bank.

He found her later at her father's lodge, and she seemed to believe him when he said he swam upon her accidentally. Just the same she stayed cautious and distant. Knowing that she loved to gamble, he invited her to a gambler's lodge, but she turned him down. Later on, he found her there with the most despised trapper at the rendezvous, a huge French-Canadian bully called Shunar, whose claim to fame was that he had killed twenty-eight men who had thought they could lick him.

Alice's luck was bad, and Kit advised her a little, which she resented. She put up and lost her beads, her moccasins, her leggings, her skirt, and finally her shirt. Before she could remove it to pay up, Kit advanced silver to cover her debt. Refusing it, Alice accepted a stake from Shunar instead.

In the morning, Alice's father came to Kit and reported that Shunar had tried to rape Alice in the night. He had been too drunk to succeed, but he had managed to cut away Alice's knotted hair girdle, which Indian maidens wore as a symbol of chastity.

After hearing the chief out, Kit sat awhile, doodling in the dust. Something had to be done about Shunar, and Kit knew that he was appointed to do it. It was not that he was braver than other men. He was as much afraid of Shunar as everyone else. But there was that compulsion within him, that will for the right, that forced him to do what had to be done.

He honed up his Green River knife, cleaned and checked his pistol, and felt his lean muscles and the rapid, anxious beat of his heart. Then he set out to find Shunar. The bearded giant was entertaining a group of trappers and Indians by boasting about how he could lick any American, Englishman, Frenchman, or German at the rendezvous. They were all yellow, he declared. Little David strode up to this Goliath.

"Shunar," Kit said, "I'm agin that kind of talk. You're a liar in the first place because you can't lick even me."

Shunar laughed at the bantam rooster and pushed him away. Kit lunged back at Shunar, striking him in the face with all his strength. With his bloated face blood-red from the slap, the giant stared a moment into Kit's turquoise eyes. Something in them made him hesitate. Then Shunar shifted his rifle to dueling position just as Kit whipped out his pistol. Pistol and rifle exploded together. Shunar's ball went high, though the powder burned Kit's eyebrows. Kit's bullet plowed through Shunar's chest, and he fell. After bleeding a minute or two from the mouth, he gave one last gurgle and died. Kit turned on his heel and strode away.

That night, as he turned and tossed in his blankets, something landed close beside him. As he jumped up, rifle in hand, he heard a girl's light laugh, and he saw a slight figure melting into the night. The thrown object was a pair of new moccasins, Kit's size. In the firelight, he saw that they bore Alice's trademark of pressed quills.

When an Indian girl gives a man moccasins, it means only one thing—she wants him. Kit dressed and rode to the lodge of Chief Running-Around-In-A-Circle. Alice's father was posted outside, as Kit knew he would be. The chief pointed to Shunar's scalp hanging from his totem, and they embraced. Kit displayed his new moccasins. He explained in bad Arapahoe that he didn't have twenty-five horses at the moment with which to buy Alice. Could he buy her little by little? Something like a giggle seemed to come from the open-skirted lodge. The old man grinned and held up one crooked finger. Just one old mule with soft feet! Kit could buy Alice for just one old mule!

The two men shook hands, and as soon as the chief vanished behind the lodge, Kit slipped inside. Alice was waiting for him, kneeling beside her blankets. She was tending a little fire on which a pot of coffee steamed. She held out her small arms to him. Christopher Carson was a married man at last.

Only one small cloud marred Kit's happiness—Joe Meek. The mere fact of Kit's marriage tended to remind Joe that he could not have his Mountain Lamb. But one day fortuitous lightning struck. Mountain Lamb arrived at the rendezvous. She went straight to Joe with a letter from her husband, Milton Sublette. Milton wrote that he was invalided with cancer in St. Louis and would be dead in a year. The letter concluded by giving Mountain Lamb to Joe with Milton's blessing.

On August 21, 1835, the two Carsons and the two Meeks joined Jim Bridger's brigade which rode north for Jackson's Hole at the east base of the Tetons.

In the months which followed, Kit wondered more and more just how long his wilderness idyll could last. Though heavy trapping had been going on for only ten years, beaver were already getting scarce in some areas. On top of that, beaver prices were slipping. People around the world were turning from beaver to silk hats.

The scarcity of beaver and the decline in prices were big worries to Kit now that he had a wife to support. And furthermore, Alice was pregnant. In an effort to find better beaver streams, he deposited her at Bent's Fort and made a fruitless trip into the barrens beyond the Great Salt Lake. In the summer of 1838, Kit returned to Alice at Bent's, and to his new baby daughter, whom he named Adaline, after his niece in Missouri. He had only a few dollars to show for more than a year of dangerous work, and he was badly discouraged. William Bent gave him a job at once as the Fort's official hunter, which raised his spirits some, until Alice fell ill. Kit felt from the start that it would be a fatal illness, and he was right. In less than a month, Alice's beauty faded away. She became a pitiful hag of skin and bones, too weak to move from Kit's lodge. In October, she died.

The loss of his Alice nearly took Kit under too. He placed little Adaline with Alice's relatives and plunged into a series of meaningless and disconnected activities. He did odd jobs at Fort Davy Crockett in Brown's Hole and led a trading expedition far south among the Navajos. He kept trying to replace Alice, the irreplaceable, getting himself into frequent woman trouble.

There was his brief marriage to a hot-mouthed Cheyenne girl of frivolous disposition. One night he came home and found her with a young Indian buck. When he started reproving her, she had a monumental tantrum and divorced him by tearing off his right moccasin and driving him from her tepee. Not long after that, he became engaged to Josefa Jaramillo, the pretty young sister of Charles Bent's wife. It tickled Kit Carson that he—an unschooled trapper from Missouri—should be accepted by the proud Jaramillo clan, who had been leaders in New Mexico society since *conquistador* days.

But Kit decided that before he and Josefa were married, he ought to arrange for the education of his daughter, Adaline. So he took Adaline to St. Louis and enrolled her in the convent which the Bent children attended.

On a Missouri River steamer, making his return trip, Kit met John Charles Frémont, who took an instant liking to him and was later largely responsible for creating the legend of the great and fabulous Kit Carson. At that time twenty-eight years old and a lieutenant in the U.S. Army Engineers, Frémont was the protegé and son-in-law of Senator Thomas Hart Benton of Missouri, the celebrated advocate of Western exploration and annexation.

It was Benton who had maneuvered the Army into sending Frémont west to map the Oregon Trail as far as South Pass— ostensibly. Frémont's undercover job was far more dramatic than making maps. His real job was to promote the senator's plans to bring the whole West under American control. Oregon must become solely American, instead of staying in the existing British-American set-up. California and New Mexico must be wrested from Mexico. The Republic of Texas must be annexed by the United States. Then millions of Americans in the cramped East could shake themselves loose and find a new life of freedom and opportunity in this western empire.

Lieutenant Frémont didn't have any trouble persuading Kit to sign up at a fat one hundred dollars a month as official guide for the First Frémont Expedition of 1842. The expedition turned out to be a three-month lark for Kit. After leading Frémont's tender crew to South Pass and back to Fort Laramie, he collected his $300, visited Bent's Fort, and went on down to Taos to marry Josefa Jaramillo. She was not yet fifteen but she had developed into a stately Spanish beauty.

Three months later, as he hurried east to check a rumor that Frémont wanted him, he met some Mexicans fearful that they would be robbed and murdered by Texas land pirates. The Mexicans offered him $150 to take word for help to General Armijo at Santa Fe. Kit said he hadn't time to double back. Just then a spring wagon drew up. Gertrudes stepped out, a little heavier than in the Burro Alley days, but handsome still in smart St. Louis clothes. She said gaily, *"Como 'sta, muchacho!"* and hugged Kit as though he were still a teenaged youngster. She asked him to make the Santa Fe trip for her sake, and he agreed. When he received his fee, he found Gertrudes had increased it to $300.

With the messenger job done, Kit got definite orders from Frémont and joined him above Bent's Fort in July of 1843. Frémont told him that this Second Frémont Expedition would map the Oregon Trail beyond South Pass to the Pacific. Kit would be the official hunter, and Tom Fitzpatrick would be the guide.

Bursting with excitement, Frémont showed Kit a twelve-pound howitzer from the St. Louis arsenal, which he had wangled somehow out of Colonel Stephen Watts Kearny. Tom Fitzpatrick led most of the expedition toward Oregon via South Pass, strictly according to government orders. But Frémont himself, with Kit and a picked group of Kit's Taos friends comprised a secret brigade which sneaked west through the Bull Pen to Green River and southwestward to Great Salt Lake in the Utah part of Northern Mexico. This brigade had the twelve-pound howitzer, in case, Frémont said, Mexican officials learned of their presence on Mexican soil and came after them.

The heavy howitzer was a damned nuisance in Kit's opinion, and he had no enthusiasm either for this excursion to Great Salt Lake. Like many Mountain Men, he had avoided it heretofore, considering it very bad medicine. Nothing could live in it, and Kit had heard frightening tales about its man-eating buzzards and about the odd way parts of it vanished for years and about the sucking whirlpool, where its waters sank in the earth to emerge hot enough to boil an egg eight hundred miles westward in the San Francisco Bay.

He liked Great Salt Lake even less when he stood on its crusted shores and stared at the gray-green water with its ominous white-caps in the distance. Proudly, Frémont unpacked a tublike rubber boat of his own design and announced that Kit, Alex Godey, and Basil Lajeunesse would accompany him on a search for the sucking whirlpool. Kit paled and told Frémont he couldn't swim a stroke. Frémont said he didn't have to swim. If the rubber boat upset, which seemed likely, Kit would float in the buoyant water like a cork.

The rubber boat was hard to propel. Kit was seasick from the start, and the other amateur tars spent so much time bailing that they paddled only nine miles in twelve hours. That was enough even for Skipper Frémont, who decided the sucking whirlpool was a myth. He landed his green-faced crew on a barren isle which he said might contain gold. This was Myth Number Two. Kit saw only dead pelicans and rotten gulls' eggs. Frémont named the stinking place Disappointment Island. A blessed breeze helped them to regain the mainland in six hours.

Early in the fall, Kit guided the secret brigade back to the main Frémont Expedition at Fort Hall on the Snake, and Fitzpatrick led them on west down the Oregon Trail to The Dalles. Frémont completed his official mission by descending the Columbia River to its mouth. All that remained was to bring his men home to St. Louis.

But, Frémont confided to Kit, the War Department had not instructed him specifically on *how* he should bring his men home. And Kit should not forget that Frémont was working as much for Senator Benton as for the U.S. Army Engineers. He had proved that Salt Lake had no outlet. But another legend asserted that a broad river flowed from the Nevada Basin through the precipitous High Sierras to sunny California. Such a river would make a fine military route some day for an American invasion of Mexico's Golden Shore. It was the plain duty of the Frémont Expedition to find this river —on its way home, wasn't it? The spirit of adventure burned in Kit as strongly as it burned in Frémont, so he agreed.

The Frémont Expedition left The Dalles on a snowflaky day in late November—25 men, 104 mules and horses, and the troublesome howitzer. Kit guided them more or less by ear down through Central Oregon to Klamath Marsh, where he turned east and south into the high bleak desert just east of the whitening Sierras. The desert degenerated into a baffling series of awesome plateaus and dead-end alkali basins. Forage became rare, and the waters were often unusable. Kit examined stream after stream for clues to the great river of the legend through the snowbound mountains to California, and finally Kit told Frémont that he was satisfied there was no such river. By this time, supplies were low. The horses and mules were so thin that Kit refused to sanction taking more blood from them as food for the men. He warned Frémont that if they didn't clear out at once and get over the Sierras into California, they would be eating their own moccasins—or each other. Then he dropped a bomb. Frémont's precious howitzer must be abandoned.

The headstrong lieutenant went into a sulk of several hours. But in the end, Frémont obeyed what amounted to an order. He dumped the clumsy thing. Even freed of it, Kit had to struggle desperately for a month to bring the expedition to the top of what would be known to future generations as Carson Pass. Under those terrible mid-February conditions, only 33 animals survived of the 104 which had left Oregon.

But Kit came through without losing a single man. Into this achievement he poured the sum of his whole life's experience with the wilderness, which he loved and understood and counted on always for salvation. His superb knowledge of how to survive and his ability to improvise in solving new problems brought a result which contrasts sharply to that of hundreds of emigrants who would die in the next few years trying to cross this range under similar handicaps of deep snow, high wind, and sub-zero temperatures.

On the easy western descent, Kit boosted the morale of the exhausted party by describing the delights of California—plenty of game, brandy, fat cattle, and luscious senoritas. The emaciated men plodded hopefully past Lake Tahoe and the American River and arrived at last in the greening paradise of the Sacramento Valley and the trading post of Captain John Sutter. At the post, Frémont bought supplies and new clothing for the ragged expedition. Then Kit led the expedition south on fresh horses, equipped with new wood saddles and huge high wooden stirrups. After crossing the Mohave Desert, they made good time through lower Nevada and Central Utah on the Spanish Trail to Fort Roubidoux, and then east past

Brown's Hole, the Bull Pen, South Park, and the Arkansas River.

The travelers reached Bent's Fort on July 1, 1844, looking so odd in their California costumes that William Bent sent scouts to identify them. Then the Fort's guns blazed a welcome, and extra flags floated above the big quadrangle. The fort's personnel got drunk in their honor, and so did swarms of Indians from the Arapahoe and Cheyenne villages.

There was good news for Lieutenant Frémont. President Tyler had promoted him from shave-tail to captain. The Bent brothers gave a banquet for the Second Frémont Expedition, after which Kit said good-bye to his friends and hurried to Taos and Josefa's arms.

He had been gone a whole year. It was, Josefa said, too long. Kit promised to change his ways. During the next several months, he bought Josefa a comfortable adobe house just off Taos Plaza and a nice ranch on the Rayado across the Sangre de Cristos. But Christopher Carson was already becoming a heroic figure, and there was little hope now that he would be allowed to change his ways. Joe Meek's exalted cousin, James K. Polk, became President of the United States in March of 1845 and was pressuring England into a treaty to make Oregon solely American territory. Kit was hearing a lot of talk about the annexation of Texas, and probably New Mexico too, with his brother-in-law, Charles Bent, as the first territorial governor.

Kit recognized the fine hands of Captain Frémont and of Frémont's father-in-law, Senator Benton, behind the expansionist agitation, and he wondered what use the two conspirators were making of the Frémont expeditions. He soon found out. One day, Josefa read to Kit the U.S. government report on both expeditions as published in the Taos paper, *El Crepusculo*. It was a joint literary effort, by John Charles Frémont and his wife, Jessie, and it described in ecstatic prose the wonders and beauties and opportunities of all the West from the Missouri through to disputed Oregon and Mexican California, and hinted that California was practically an independent state already and could be detached from Mexico without the least trouble.

Kit was enthralled by those glowing passages, but dismayed by the way the authors had built their whole case for western expansion around a single hero. This miraculous person was Christopher Carson, a veritable meat-axe of a man, bull-chested, great-shouldered, one hell of a fellow. They mentioned Kit's marksmanship, woodsmanship, horsemanship, and Indianship. They wrote exactly of his rescue work in the High Sierras and inexactly of his seamanship on Great Salt Lake. They glamorized his routine habit of sleeping with a charged rifle and his way of darning moccasins with thongs from his pants. All in all, they did him up brown.

When Josefa finished reading the long report, Kit said faintly, "Them fellas laid it on a mite thick." He was really appalled, but he would have been much more so had he known that the report was being summarized in virtually every American newspaper and issued in book form as a sensational best-seller. Little did he realize that this fabulous Kit Carson of Frémont's fertile and designing imagination, this legendary wilderness man of heroic proportions, was well on the way to becoming one of America's most celebrated and best-loved figures.

In August of 1845, Captain Frémont requested Kit's services a third time. More map-making in Oregon, of course. And a visit to Sutter's Fort to make sure that the Mexicans weren't mistreating the handful of American settlers in that northern end of California.

The following summer, Kit led the Third Frémont Expedition to Klamath Lake, where they were joined by an official U.S. government messenger from Washington. The messenger brought a letter from President Polk explaining that the United States and Mexico were on the verge of war on the issue of Texas annexation. The moment this war started, the Third Frémont Expedition would become automatically a fighting unit of the U.S. Army Mounted Riflemen, under Colonel John Charles Frémont, formerly Captain Frémont, and Lieutenant Christopher Carson, formerly Kit Carson, civilian guide.

Since this letter was six months old, Captain Frémont decided instantly that the Mexican War was in progress. He proclaimed himself Colonel Frémont and set out with his brand-new shave-tail, Lieutenant Carson, and his sixty mounted riflemen to take possession of Northern California. Meanwhile, U.S. warships steamed into Monterey Bay, and on July 19, a U.S. Navy battalion under Commodore Stockton joined Colonel Frémont, Lieutenant Carson, and the mounted riflemen at the gates of Monterey. Commodore Stockton gave the mounted riflemen the honor of taking the town. Frémont, lean and stern, strode down the main street at the head of his motley crew of conquerors.

A week later, Frémont's riflemen and Commodore Stockton's sailors sailed south and spent a day disarming Mexican troops at Los Angeles. The commodore named Frémont the military governor of the new American territory of California, and Frémont prepared a triumphant dispatch for President Polk describing his conquest. He ordered Kit to get the dispatch to Washington in properly dramatic style by delivering it in a record-breaking sixty days. To make this possible, Frémont assigned to Kit an outsized pack train of his finest mules and horses. Three days short of Santa Fe, Kit saw a great dust cloud ahead. It turned out to be an American regiment under General (lately Colonel) Stephen Watts Kearny, fresh from the conquest of New Mexico. His guide was none other than Tom Fitzpatrick. Kearny told Kit that Santa Fe and Taos had fallen without bloodshed, and he had appointed Charles Bent governor. Now he was on his way to seize California from Mexico.

But, Kit said, California had been seized already by Colonel Frémont who was in charge there at this very moment as military governor.

The general, a gravely courteous man of great composure, seemed a trifle upset, but after a moment, he said:

"I am afraid Colonel Frémont has exceeded his orders. I am instructed in writing by President Polk to seize that province and to assume office as military governor. Since my present guide, Mr. Fitzpatrick, is unfamiliar with the route, you will face about and guide us the rest of the way."

Stunned out of speech, Kit managed a bad salute and walked off, a baffled, miserable man. He considered ignoring Kearny, continuing his exciting trip, and relying on Senator Benton to protect him from court-martial. But he couldn't. A general of the United States Army must be obeyed. He gave Frémont's dispatches to Fitzpatrick, and turned around unhappily toward the Golden Shore.

Kearny's plan was to join forces with Commodore Stockton's sailors at San Diego. But before his regiment got there, Alex Godey arrived to warn him that Frémont's conquest had backfired. The Mexicans had retaken everything in the south except San Diego while Colonel Frémont was away someplace bear hunting.

Kit urged Kearny to drive on San Diego in compact Mountain Man fashion with outriders. Instead, Kearny split his forces and found his entire command trapped by Mexican guerrillas. Kit thought it served the old goat right, but of course he couldn't stand by and let the regiment be massacred. So he and another volunteer, Lieutenant Edward Beale, crawled by night through a two-mile cordon of Mexicans to get word to San Diego. The terrain was mostly cactus. They lost their shoes and had to run barefoot through the darkness for thirty miles. Beale reached San Diego delirious and unable to stand. Kit's feet were so badly cut up that Commodore Stockton held him in sick bay for weeks.

But a sailor force got through to relieve Kearny's regiment, and the combined outfits reoccupied Los Angeles and re-established Frémont's conquest. General Kearny set up his offices as military governor. Pretty soon, Colonel Frémont returned from bear hunting and resumed *his* office as military governor.

Kit's next few weeks under his old commander depressed him terribly. Frémont, normally so gay and debonair, had become as sour as a wormy old squaw. His irrational pigheadedness, his childish insistence on having his own way, led him to ignore General Kearny's Presidential orders. He would not hand over his mounted riflemen. He would not even admit that General Kearny existed. He just moped around, letting the evidence pile up which would end in his court-martial and dismissal from the service.

Kit was greatly relieved when Frémont instructed him for the second time to take dispatches to President Polk in Washington. Once again, he crossed the now familiar Mohave Desert happy at the thought of being able to see his friends at Bent's Fort and spend a few hours again with Josefa. But he was due for still another shock and this time a severe one. While still on the trail, he learned that insurrection had broken out around Taos.

On a gray January dawn, a band of Pueblo Indians and Mexicans broke into the Bent home, scalped Charles, chopped off his head, and carried it away. The nightgowned Jaramillo girls—wives of Bent, Kit Carson, and Tom Boggs—and Bent's terrified children cowered in a corner, expecting to be murdered any moment themselves. But for some strange reason, the women and children were spared, and remaining all night beside the headless body, they slipped away to safety.

Many of Kit's American friends died violently on that bloody day. But Ceran St. Vrain mustered a furious force which stormed the adobe church in which the rebels were forted. St. Vrain and his men killed fifty-one of the fifty-four inside. Ceran himself scalped the leader, who was wearing Governor Bent's coat.

It was a sad homecoming for Kit after twenty months' absence from Josefa. But after a few days with her, he was compelled to continue on east with Frémont's dispatches.

In St. Louis, he bought a stiff dragoon cap, wool trousers, and a tight long-skirted coat. He observed with shy wonder and embarrassment that everyone recognized him as the hero of the Frémont report. When he dined at the Rocky Mountain House, crowds gathered outside. He was lionized on the steamer to Wheeling, on the stage to Cumberland, and on the B. & O. train to Washington.

Jessie Frémont met him at the Washington station and took him to her home and, knowing how to treat a Mountain

Man, gave him breezy quarters on an open verandah. Kit delivered Frémont's dispatches to President Polk, who had quite a little chat with him and ended the audience by giving Kit his commission as a lieutenant in the Mounted Riflemen. Up to then, Kit had only Frémont's word for it.

That mission didn't end Kit's dispatch-bearing career. It went on for many months, until he was good and sick of it. When the Mexican War ended, he quit cold and hurried home to Taos. He quit partly because he had had all he could take of the Army, and he quit also in a huff upon learning that the U.S. Senate had refused to ratify his lieutenant's commission. The reason was guilt by association. Kit had worked with the discredited Colonel Frémont.

But mostly he quit because the time had come, had really come, to settle down. He was thirty-eight years old, and his stocky figure was beginning to bulge a little around the middle. He'd die now if he had to run all night to escape a Comanche war party. So he trailed home to Taos and faithful Josefa and set about raising a large family—seven children in all by Josefa; the first-born was named Charles, in memory of Charles Bent.

Although he'd settled himself down to ranching across the Sangre de Cristos, next to Lucien Maxwell's vast spread, he was still a sort of volunteer detective and trigger man for anyone within three hundred miles who had dangerous but honest work to do. A big army supply post, Fort Union, was built near the Carson ranch, and the West Pointers kept asking Kit to solve their frequent Indian problems. When the Apaches massacred most of the White caravan, Kit led the pursuit, though the soldiers closed in too slowly and Chief Lobo had time to murder the captive Mrs. White. When the Fox gang planned to hold up a rich wagon train, Kit headed the army unit which captured the bandits.

In 1852, Kit and Lucien Maxwell went off for some weeks on a sentimental trapping journey to South Park, the Bull Pen, and the Laramie Plains. And in 1853, the two old friends and Tom Boggs, Kit's brother-in-law, drove thirteen thousand sheep all the way from the Rayado to San Francisco via Fort Laramie and the Overland Trail.

Kit cleared $12,000 on the drive, the one financial killing of his career.

A high honor came to him as he got back home to Josefa. He was appointed U.S. Indian Agent at Taos for the Southern Utes and Apaches, and stayed on as a revered Indian Agent until the Civil War began.

When Fort Sumter was fired on, he raised the Stars and Stripes in Taos Plaza, shook hands with his Taos friend, Major Sibley, who left to join the Confederates, and signed up as a leader of the New Mexican Volunteers.

Colonel Carson's cavalry fought and lost to Sibley's force at Valverde below Santa Fe in February, 1862. A month later, the Colorado Volunteers rushed down from Denver and defeated Sibley at Glorieta Pass, ending the Confederate threat to capture Fort Union and the whole Southwest.

Meanwhile, the sporadic Indian War continued. Colonel Carson and his soldiers were assigned to cleaning up pockets of hostile red men. First, Kit corraled the White Mountain Apaches and placed them in Fort Sumter. Next, he drove the proud Navajos from their allegedly impregnable fortress deep in the Canon de Chelly, west of Taos, and delivered them to Fort Canby.

But Kit's third and last Indian campaign ended in failure, the one bad beating of his life. In late November of 1864, he was sent with four hundred soldiers to wipe out a winter camp of Comanches and Kiowas at a west Texas spot called Adobe Walls. After two days of fighting, Kit had to call a retreat to Fort Bascom. This battle demonstrated the growing strength and determination of the Plains Indians in their desperate last stand for freedom.

It demonstrated something else too; Kit's wiry body was failing, and rapidly. Some time earlier, he had been dragged and mauled by a horse. Now he had chest pains and head-aches. He was glad to be relieved of field duty and assigned to Fort Garland in Colorado's San Luis Valley. Josefa was with him, and his six small children who romped around the post like a herd of wild colts.

One day, word came that he had been brevetted a brigadier-general. General Christopher Carson! Though Kit cared little for most honors, this one pleased him. But he hated to be addressed as "General." Off the post, he made everyone call him plain "Kit." Just before retiring in 1867, Kit took time out to learn to write a little. A general, he told Josefa, should be able at least to sign his own name.

His heart pains grew worse. They were caused by an aneurism of the aorta, according to Dr. Tilton, surgeon at Fort Lyon down on the Arkansas. To be near Tilton, Kit moved with Josefa and the children to Tom Boggs' settlement. He was forbidden to ride now, and yet life passed pleasantly. He played an endless game with his children, lying on the ground while they hunted through his pockets for candy. Old friends from Fort Lyon called daily. He reminisced for them in his high, gentle voice, his solemn face dead-pan, and his gray eyes turning turquoise when the action got fast.

What bothered him most were the constant evidences of his fame. Government maps bearing his name appeared— Carson Valley, Utah; Carson Sink and Carson Lake, Nevada; Carson Pass, California. He would shake his gray head with tired displeasure and mutter, "Now why'd they do that fer?" And if he lived now, he would ask it again, seeing his name plastered all over the West, on schools, riding clubs, national forests, city parks, counties and towns, cemetaries, railroad cars, and military camps. "Now why'd they do that fer?"

And after all, why did they do it?

Kit Carson wasn't handsome or husky or graceful. A hundred other Mountain Men could ride as well, shoot as well, fight as well, guide as well, explore as well. Some of them— Jim Bridger, Tom Fitzpatrick, Jed Smith, and a dozen more— were his superiors in mountaineering skill.

But Kit had something more than all the rest. He had the unswerving will to carry on against any odds and any hazards, just as they did, but he also had a special kind of vividly active, creative imagination, combined with the practical ability to apply it when and where it was desperately needed. He also had an abiding and unshakable faith in himself and a sympathetic, confident grasp of his environment.

All of these things made him a living symbol of the restless, searching, dauntless pioneer spirit that pushed our frontier across the plains, over the Rockies, and down to the vast Pacific shoreline. As such a symbol, his shy, unassuming, almost meek personality had a tremendous impact, and it was inevitable that even in his lifetime many persons who knew him for exactly what he was were busily and happily engaged in making of him a monumental legend of heroic proportions.

In March of 1868, Kit journeyed against Tilton's orders to Washington to help some Utes get money due them from the government. On his return, the faithful, self-effacing Josefa died in childbirth, aged thirty-nine. Worn out, sick, and sorrowing, Kit was faced with the problem of caring for three boys and four girls. (Adaline had married long since and gone to California.) He had little money left.

The Jaramillos and Bents, the Boggs and St. Vrains and Maxwells, rallied around. Kit must not worry. His children would be looked after. He was consoled some.

In mid-May of 1868, with the cottonwoods leafing and the orioles flashing orange in the willows, Dr. Tilton carried him to an infirmary room at Fort Lyon. Kit refused to lie on the bed and demanded a straw pallet on the floor. He suffered horribly from coughing, which, Tilton warned, would finally kill him by hemorrhage or suffocation.

Kit dictated his will, disposing of a few cattle and the Taos house. He asked Tom Boggs to bury him with Josefa at Taos.

On the afternoon of May 23, he gave some coins to his small boys, Willie and Charlie, with which to buy hats. Charlie dropped his coins and lost them wading the Arkansas, but Kit wouldn't scold him. He just gave him some more. Toward evening, he felt hungry and ordered a steak for dinner. He ate it all and lighted his old pipe. He joked feebly with Tilton and with Aloys Scheurich, his niece's husband. A bull-bat squeaked.

Suddenly Kit coughed. He took Scheurich's hand.

"I'm gone," Kit said. "Good-bye, Doctor. *Adios, compadre.*"

The end came quickly.